MOTHER'S
DAY
IN THE
EMPIRE STATE
OR,
AN ANSWER TO THE
ARRAIGNMENT
OF
WOMEN

WWW.FREE-GRACEPRESS.COM

ISBN 978-1-7321669-0-5 (audio book)
ISBN 978-1-7321669-1-2 (hard cover)
ISBN 978-1-7321669-2-9 (paperback)
ISBN 978-1-7321669-3-6 (ebook)

First edition.

www.Free-Gracepress.com

MOTHER'S DAY IN THE EMPIRE STATE OR, AN ANSWER TO THE ARRAIGNMENT OF WOMEN

by

Constantia Munda

2024

CONTENTS

Free-Grace Press is proud to publish its second novel titled "**Mother's Day in the Empire State, Or An Answer to The Arraignment of Women**," which is our second novel answering the misogynist pamphlet written by Joseph Swetnam in 1615, titled "**The Arraignment of Leuud, Idle, Froward, and Unconstant Women: Or the Vanitie of Them, Choose You Whether: With a Commendation of Wise, Vertuous and Honest Women: Pleasant for Married Men, Profitable for Young Men, and Hurtfull to None**."

In the polemic spirit of Jane Anger's "**The Protection for Women**" (1589), we publish as a rebuttal to Swetnam's pamphlet "**Mother's Day in the Empire State, Or An Answer to the Arraignment of Women**," written by **Constantia "Connie" Munda**. Free-Grace Press publishes this deposition novel investigating three very distinct stories about motherhood in America. This novel was found within the Public Records of the Allegheny Family Court in the New York Empire State. It is a deposition from the author, illustrator, and Child Protective Services officer Constantia "Connie" Munda.

By publishing "**Mother's Day in the Empire State, Or An Answer to the Arraignment of Women**," we hope to unearth child abuse wherever it exists and to expose it. This novel also investigates "**The family**," patriarchy, breeding, "*Love*" and/or "**The Expectant Mother Racket**," as Anna Jarvis (the founder of Mother's Day in 1906) called the modern-day family.

Woman especially are preyed upon to succumb to the "**Expectant Mother Racket**" because Mother's Day originally was about mothers meeting and working together to end wars and war-mongering governments. Anna Jarvis did not believe in the "Sentimentalizing of motherhood" – and according to **Anna Jarvis**, "**Motherhood is a man-made invention**" by "**Mother's Day Imposters**" and "**Charity Charlatans**."

Anna Jarvis FOUNDED THE MOTHER'S DAY HOLIDAY AS AN ANTI-WAR HOLIDAY FOR WOMEN to organize against war-mongering politicians and governments who sent their children to war. "Mother's Day in the Empire State, Or An Answer to the Arraignment of Women" will give the reader the intelligence, the illustrations, and data to prove that American "Motherhood" is child abuse.

Literally, graphically, and linguistically, Free-Grace Press publishes this deposition novel as the second part of a five-novel series about Free-Grace philosophy via the **Artist's Book**. Our first Artist's Book novel was published in 2018 and is titled "**The Worming of America, Or An Answer to the Arraignment of Women**," by **Autumn Leaf**. It's an Artist's Book designed and published in the style of William Blake's "Songs of Innocence and Experience" (1794). We also acknowledge Laurence Sterne's "The Life and Opinions of Tristram Shandy, Gentleman" (1759) in which the graphics and a modern flat arc is explored with prose concerned more about philosophy, language, the fine arts, architecture, and humanity than a standard plot. Literally, "**Mother's Day in the Empire State, Or An Answer to the Arraignment**

of Women" is also inspired by Clarice Lispector's "The Passion According to G.H." (1964) in which a woman's metaphysical and psychological breakdown is revealed.

The "**Mother's Day in the Empire State**" novel has a relatively flat arc with only one repeat, a mash-up, and a deceptive closure. In lyrical algebra the novel has an unexpected long opening, then goes into a repeat for the majority of the novel. At Chapter 17 there is a denouement mash-up, and then the novel ends quickly with a deceptive closure. The novel's chapter's algebraic rhyme structure is as follows:

A B A B A C D E D E D E D E D-E D E C.

Constantia "Connie" Munda has written a tragic-comedy deposition. In one large part, it is a treatise to our English-thinking soul about why we are killing our children, and in another smaller part, Connie has created a theater of the absurd. The free-verse, satirical prose evokes the languid and serious style of Virginia Woolf woven together with poetic folly and stream of consciousness for the right side of your brain. Dialogue and descriptions are reminiscent of Voltaire, Flannery O'Connor, and Walt Whitman.

Free-Grace Press believes the worst reading is to have prose with no answers, no expected rhythm, or an unorthodox measure, yet ambiguity and unanswered questioning drive the pulse and rhythm of this "Mother's Day" novel. Connie Munda, the narrator, jumps around from the storyline to fine art, philosophy, stream of consciousness, and history, not just using **Haikus,** but **Haibuns** with a Metafiction prose for the early 21st century.

For Free-Grace Press, the literary prosimetrum meter becomes not just an expressive tool, a "**Mathesis**" style, but altogether - a **Mathemaku** style. This

Metafiction and *Mathemaku* style are not just Post-Modern and Hyper-Modern, but a **Meta-Modern style.**

Our **Meta-Modern** style is "Writerly" in Roland Barthes (French Literary Philosopher) terms, and Free-Grace Press continues to answer Barthes' two important essays: "The Last Happy Writer" (Voltaire) 1964 and "The Death of the Author," 1967. Our books make the reader an active participant in the novel. The text is free, not restrictive, and encourages the reader to slow down and use their imagination / the right side of their brain.

Our "Mother's Day in the Empire State" novel is a true deposition, but not a true deposition. Correct or incorrect is not the issue, but our life, our future, and our children's soul is the issue. The novel adopts no standard form, moving itself toward a vibrant individual prose and novel style.

Constantia Munda, our narrator and author, investigates two mothers for child abuse on Mother's Day in 2021. Connie believes both mothers investigated seem to play a male-heroic, martyr role, and/or Jesus role, not using their feminine energy. So, Connie the author has structured this novel's chapters alongside the crucifixion of Christ and/or **The Stations of the Cross.**

Connie Munda is a single mother of two children, a veteran Military Intelligence officer, and a Child Protective Services (CPS) officer. Connie brings her troubled and noble female heredity as the granddaughter of Anna Jarvis – the West Virginia woman who started Mother's Day in 1906. **The Mother's Day Holiday was originally an Anti-War day for mothers to gather and set up political opposition to WAR, because war only kills a mother's child.**

Connie brings her worldly, razor-sharp mathematical "Intelligence" descriptions and examinations of two abusive mothers within Appalachian and "Upstate

Chapter 1

INTRODUCTIONS, COMMENTS, SUGGESTIONS

This Deposition is from May 9th, 2021, and it is
being prepared in response to **Complaint #21-4532**
and **Complaint #21-6154**. Both child abuse complaints
come from the Town of Allegheny, New York. They are
anonymous complaints about two (2) mothers abusing their children. My name is Officer Constantia
"Connie" Munda, and my badge number is three one
four (#314). I've been a Child Protection Specialist
(CPS) for twelve (12) years in the New York Empire
State.

DEPOSITION TRANSCRIPT BEGINS:
5-9-21, 12:09 a.m.

Dear Honorable Family Court and Good Reader: I'm
driving way too fast and it's a little after midnight, the beginning of Mother's Day in the New York
Empire State. The moon on my western horizon plays
games with me and the silvery clouds that are moving in my same westerly direction. "Going West" here
in northern Appalachia is the prevailing wind both
physically and metaphysically. The American pilgrim
traffic has been so thick here for the spiritual and
financially desperate and their families for the

1
2
3
4
5
6
7
8
9
10
11
12
13
14
15
16
17
18
19
20
21
22
23
24
25

last two hundred and thirty-four (234) years that this land has been called the "Scorched earth."

I'm in an unmarked retired State Trooper car, and I'm recording my Family Court Deposition on my ear hook with microphone. I will attach this Deposition transcript and approximately fifteen (15) People's Exhibits for the Family Court and Good Reader. I'm leaving the Albany Capitol region and heading west as many pilgrims have in the past – towards the infamous Seneca Indian Great Hill and its Western Door to America.

My target Town of Allegheny sits on the threshold of this doorway. My Empire State car, number two zero four (#204), a Trooper car converted to a Child Protective Services (CPS) undercover car, is a Ford(F) Interceptor. Low and heavy with excellent engineering, this Mad Max car easily slices through the rolling hills of the Susquehanna River valleys. River roads shaded in a purple-black, bruised and sleepy from a long winter roll away, winding along with the Chemung River. These Appalachian hills form a hallway valley to my moonlit Western Door for scorched-earth America and all its Great Awakenings.

This path was not just blazed, but the earth was scorched by the American patriot's Sullivan Expedition in 1779. Might was proven right to the six (6) Iroquois Indian Nation Tribes who mistakenly sided with the British Empire, both in the American Revolution in 1776 and The War of 1812. Then in 1830, the Western Door became a spiritual pilgrim holy land and path to spiritual experiments championing utopias, Christianity, slave's rights, and women's rights. There were the Shakers, the Quakers, the Latter-Day Saints (LDS – the Mormons), the Adventists, the Chautauquans, and even the Jehovah's Witnesses. This antebellum Appalachia is a burned-over wormhole now; spirituality and culturally it's an "Upstate" void, a blackhole, and/or "Nothing."

I crack my car window to get some fresh air and stay alert. The Appalachian air is filled with emerald-green pine swamps, bloody dead possums, and skunks in heat. The night air is deeply haunted at this time of night, but I want to start my CPS surveillance and investigations around three-thirty *ante meridiem* (3:30 a.m.) in the morning. It's peaceful here in the nighttime with these enchanted little mountains rolling behind... if you're okay with ghosts, anything is possible here.

Traveling west into northern Appalachia is similar to going off the grid or slipping around in the night of a third-world country with the American military. Black operations function out of black operations that function out of black operations, which only destroys "Us" and strengthens "Them." It's black and fast here in northern Appalachia as I float back into our primordial cave and our lives become timeless and entangled.

I try to get in the spirit of Appalachia and put my worn-out compact disc (CD) of Faith Hill and Tim McGraw singing nostalgically about beers in the fridge, muddy boots, and desperate house-for-sale signs going up back home in Appalachia. I think the song is called "Back at Mama's."

The spring has not yet come to the Southern Tier. The frigid Canadian air with "Lake Effect" freezes my nostrils and washed hair. I roll up my car window and turn the heat up to eighty-eight (88) degrees. My exterior thermometer reads twenty-eight (28) degrees as I smell my hair / my favorite henna conditioner. The smell reminds me that I need to order more, as I've already watered it down. The weather here on Mother's Day in May in the North Country is still like late March for the rest of America (Lows: twenty-five (25) degrees, and Highs: forty-eight

(48) degrees). It's cold and spooky here... especially with the supernatural *Ides of March* lingering perpetually here in shadows of north Appalachia. Here on May 9th, 2021, only a few spring flowers – mostly daffodils – have pushed through for Mother's Day 2021, but there is plenty of mud pushing up our frost heaves.

I come from West Virginia, so I'm not used to these low temperatures in May. Let me tell you Family Court and all you non-Yankee readers out there with thin blood like mine: There is something even more horrible than blizzards and the cold winter season that the sadomasochist Yankees seem to enjoy.

In New England and "Upstate" New York there is something to live for after being incarcerated for five (5) months (mid-November to mid-April). Imprisoned by four (4) feet of snow and not confined in your bright, airy large home, but in your ten by ten (10 x 10) bedroom. There one sits in a windowless black igloo that resembles a homeless cardboard camp under a bridge or a lame Burning-Man (BM) camp. Here in this cold discontent, one has to look forward to a "Mud Season." There one sits shivering even in April and May when your ten-by-ten (10 x 10) bedroom with a space heater between your legs is still your only home.

Your home used to be your well-lit, spacious two-thousand (2,000) square-foot home, but no northern Yankee can or will afford to heat their whole house. If you thought wet snow was hard to shovel, just wait until you have to dig out your car from soft wet mud up to its axles.

The gray sun doesn't win in *Upstate* America; even now in May, the air smells like wet earth and decomposing leaves. The overall landscape color is that of old, bad, red meat or dried blood. It's raw, wet, and chilling to the bone here in northern

Appalachia, even in the shadows of hot and muggy August.

I forgot how talky (annoying?) Tim McGraw is in the beginning of this big Mama song, but when Faith Hill comes in and harmonizes, she changes the song from a whiny redneck leaning on the back of his pick-up to a beautiful ballad. Unfortunately, Faith Hill is only whispering in this song, but the slide guitar keeps you tuned in. And then the ooo- ooo- ooohs hit... I'm in the middle of the ooohs right now – this is a musical denouement if I've ever heard one. I slide my car window down going seventy-six miles per hour (76 mph) and yell to the possums, coons, and Appalachian blackness, "Hey soundman, turn up the Faith! Because everyone needs Faith in Appalachia!"

There is leftover brown snow here in the shadows from the mid-April Nor'easter blizzard from a few weeks back that dumped three (3) feet of wet snow on *Us*. Along the roadside, yellow daffodils are being dusted with snow that looks like confection-er's sugar on golden caramel candies. Regardless, I can smell the red and brown leaves dying / compost-ing and an Appalachian summer coming. But spring in Appalachia... a cloudy leftover embarrassment from a St. Patrick's Day party lingers till sum-mertime with bloody knives still being twisted and muddy tires still spinning. Here in the Southern Tier, the winter is never really gone — it lives in the earth and the icy rocks like an evil tradition transposed into a new holiday.

So, thank the Lord for my warm Ford Interceptor. Aagghh, the luxury of going seventy-six miles per hour (76 mph) and feeling like I'm at home in my bathtub with a glass of Chianti. A wet Finger Lake chill runs up my lady-like pant leg, and I curse myself for not wearing heavier leggings. I turn up the heat in the car. Peering out into the darkness: the millions of stars are burning bright tonight as

I drive west into a land darker than any night sky in New England or the northeast. The white glow of my dashboard instrument lighting is calm and discreet.

My car smells and tastes like a brand-new car even though this New York State Trooper car was decommissioned seven (7) years ago. A cold Canadian wind blows snow flurries across my windshield as the Empire Troopers (every five (5) exits) clock me doing seventy-three miles per hour (73 mph) in a fifty-five-mile-per-hour (55 mph) zone. The Troopers have automobile license plate readers, and they instantaneously know I am the Empire Law – I am one of *Them*.

There's a seventy-five percent (75%) chance of two (2) to three (3) inches of snow by dawn. This was my spring radar for Mother's Day 2021 in Appalachia. Not just physical and emotional traps, but speed-traps and honey-traps around every hidden corner and on every exit.

Honorable Family Court, and Dear Reader, I cannot submit this "Mother's Day Madness" deposition without telling you my own motherly stories.

My grandmother was Anna Jarvis from West Virginia, and she started the Mother's Day Holiday in America in 1908 as an anti-war holiday for women and mothers.

Thirty-five (35) years later, she was forcefully institutionalized because the floral industry, chocolate industry, and war industry didn't think her Mother's Day anti-war Holiday was profitable – or "American."

My grandmother told me these industries smeared, litigated, and grinded Grandma Jarvis into the grave. The floral industry, chocolate industry, and the war industry publicly ridiculed her a "Crazy woman." They assassinated her great character and branded her NOT a "Good mother." But please mark my words, Family Court and Good Reader: before she was incarcerated, Anna Jarvis vibrated and burned brighter than any other human I've ever met.

Anna Jarvis is in fact the person who named me Constantia Munda. She said in Latin it meant "Constant Perseverance." My grandma, or Mom, as I call her sometimes – because my real mom was never really around – was a nurse in West Virginia during the American Civil War. Grandma Jarvis was a doctor's amputee assistant. Granny used to say in her *lovely* southern Appalachian drawl, "I sawed off more young men's limbs with my hacksaw than a Kentucky chicken farmer."

This was Grandma Jarvis's daytime / teatime / bourbon-time folly, but I was awoken many nights as a child by Grandma Jarvis screaming on the floor in some type of trance. I'd run to her elegant bedroom, and she would be sleepwalking or more like sleep-sawing. Grandma in the pitch-black darkness would be kneeling on the floor or leaning over a table, wrestling with something. Grandma Jarvis would be talking / yelling in some guttural alien language that sounded like she was speaking backwards, but somehow, I telepathically understood her. Grandma Anna would yell at me as she physically fought the wounded soldier. I was trying to hold down the wriggling young man as my grandma sawed his shredded and disfigured legs off. She would be yelling at me to get on me knees next to her, which I did as she was undulating with the writhing man who would walk no more. I would play along and hold my man's leg as my mother's hacksaw teeth picked, nicked, and sawed a God-made invention off a beautiful man. All for a man-made war.

After years of playing along with Grandma Anna and her nightmares, I noticed a glow or aberration of the ghostly Union soldier's spirit as we had him pinned down on the makeshift operating table. And then after my grandma cut one leg off – I heard a sickening thud as it hit the hollow wooden floor in the old grand house.

Grandma and I went to work on the other leg. I was looking at her, trying to control the man, and then slowly I started to feel the man's leg in my hands. I recoiled in horror; the ghostly insanity of war was in me. My grandma yelled at me again, "Stop being a prude and hold this soldier down!" I grabbed hold of the leg and could feel my mother's saw ripping flesh and muscle away from the bone like a dull wooden saw cutting through brown let-tuce and lard. The soldier screamed in terror! And then Grandma Jarvis's saw quickly hit the bone, and the soldier fought for his life, but his past life was a lost cause.

I remember holding thick wood – two by fours (2 x 4s) for my carpenter father when he would cut *Them* – and a human leg is no different than a two by four (2 x 4). The block of wood or the stump of leg makes the same noise when it hits the floor. The bad-end / the dumb-end noise says, "I'm dead now and best thrown in the fire."

The leg lay on my mother's bedroom floor like a struggling fish wriggling on a floating dock. I tried to grab the leg, but it wiggled out of my hands like a fish gasping for air / for life. My grandmother continued to hold and ride the young man's shoulders – she wrestled the stumped soldier to the wooden floor. I finally grabbed the leg, but I was frozen and paralyzed as my dead-fish limb slowly died in my hands. I could feel its heartbeat fade: thump-thump, thump-thump, thum-thum, thum... Thum... Thum... Thu... Th.... It was unbearable and unspeakable.

My grandma yelled in that strange guttural alien language again. My Granny cried to the man and cra-dled him as he fell to the floor and curled into a fetal position. Mom sung in lullaby tones in that

disturbing language to the soldier who would stroll
no more. My hands felt wet – drenched in blood. I
put my bloody hand on my mom's shoulder to wake her.
I shook her, and there was nothing there in the dark
bedroom except my grandmother and a Yankee paraple-
gic groaning in pain – asking God to kill him.

"God almighty, I'm sorry... God almighty please
don't let we walk the earth a war-cripple! Please
kill me!!!" There was silence, but I swear to my
Maker, I swear to this Family Court, and I swear
to you, Dear Reader – I heard another man laughing. Laughing quietly, who said, "I told you so,
hero-boy, but you didn't listen... enjoy your
wheelchair."

God was laughing at *Us*... covered in blood, living in misery. I died a little bit right then and
there, because I suddenly realized God our Creator
was uncaring, malicious, and vindictive. I shook my
grandma more violently, and all I could hear was
lullabies, groaning, and laughing. I ran out of her
bedroom that night unable to wake her. I never went
back into my grandmother's bedroom, and as for her
nightmares, I allowed her to wrestle those demons
alone. I'm an eternal and infinite coward for that.
I'm a bad granddaughter and a bad nurse, and –
let's get this out of the way – I'm a bad mother.

And all bad parents can take *my* litmus test to see
if they have failed at raising *their* young: Think
back to when you graduated high school or college
and think about the opportunities you had at your
doorstep. Now, on the other hand, let's look at the
opportunities your children have at the same stage
of their lives. If your children have fewer opportunities for food, clothing, and shelter than you
did, then you're a parental failure. You're a mom-
my-mooch and a deadbeat dad because you've either
devolved or you let society devolve.

And bad mothers usually aim to be a great lady

like my Granny Anna Jarvis, and while she wasn't necessarily a good mother, she was a great lady. Unfortunately, the flower, chocolate, greeting card, and military capitalists put her in the sanitarium because her idea of parenting was different than Americans' idea of "Motherhood." Those "Judeo-Christian pirates" (my grandma's language – not mine) couldn't pigeonhole my grandmother into an "*Eve*" or a "*Mary*."

Motherhood for war is where my mother died. On the other side of the scale: mother without war is a special place, a safe place, a friendly place. But sorry to say, my mother died in solitary confinement with few friends or associates in a dirty padded room in a Philadelphia nuthouse. Regardless, I still have her letters, which I carry with me in my old Air Force satchel.

Was my mother crazy? Was my mother abusive? Am I abusive? Am I crazy? Well, what mother is not crazy and abusive who lives within an Empire. Our "Red-Queen" capitalism and *Mother's Day Madness* is just part of the patriarchal game.

Is this a woman question – a *querelle des femmes*? The failure of the female mind / the creative soul, the white yin, is in question. Is there a cognitive bias? Are our processing strategies being arraigned under laws not seen to *Us*? And *our* enemy – the misogynist *Them* – is it all men, or do women also relish their own subjugation? Has our room, lock, and allowance for freedom been revoked? Has femininity been evicted to the basement, to the toolshed, or are we living under the highway in the homeless camp?

Has the hardy male cockroach – decapitated but still alive with festering sexism that hides in our society – been reincarnated after we killed it? I stepped on it and felt its ribcage being crushed under the ball of my foot. My foot's nerve endings felt the cockroach die, and the frequency was quantized terror. The cockroach oozed white goo from its crushed body, and I licked at it. The kill sent electricity up through my chakras, slowly... one by one, eventually reaching my third-eye soul. At that moment, it felt like someone, or something, had just flipped a switch and turned me off. My once-bright constitution and soul was moldy and sleazy now, yet I can still see and feel the fat roach's antennae moving slowly; I can still hear and feel his heartbeat; I still feel his masculine eyes – dead and reptilian – gazing at me... judging me... objectifying me... waiting in the shadows.

The vividness of value depends on our motherly "Intelligence" or *Intel* gathered. Besides an absence of evidence and the cumulative effect of probabilities, humanity / civilization and mothers in particular have a preference for killing their children. Perhaps this is not a women question? But it is definitely a *Red-Queen* question, a selfish-gene question. A cockroach question... and not a woman question. What is the difference? My human *Intelligence* (HUMINT) is the most defensible *Intel,* yet within *Intelligence* there is no motherly *Intelligence.*

My evolutionary future is controlled by my past, and I look at the past through my grandmother's letters. The first letter I hold dear is filed chronologically as one of the oldest – from 1892 – and it is from my grandmother, Anna Jarvis, to me, Connie Munda. As I said, she was a nurse during the Civil War, but stitched up both Confederate and Union soldiers back in West Virginia because the State was divided on slavery.

Anna, my grandmother, started the "Mother's Day Work Clubs" in 1908, declaring, "Mother's Day is a day outside the house for mothers so they can unite as a political force against raising sons and daughters for war."

My grandmother was a potent and progressive woman, but my grandmother was swimming against the times.

I have this letter tucked in my old military satchel from Air Force boot camp. Yes, I'm a military woman, which is an oxymoron I suppose — a creator within the business of killing. M-8888 is written in permanent marker – notating the first letter of my last name and the last four of my social security number – on the outside of this satchel. I like M-8888 graphically and metaphysically. It makes me realize my starting point alphabetically and numerically in America – my foundation in America: M-8888. Before the military, I was low-class dust in America, but now I was a player on the matrix / on the graph. I was a coordinate on the war axis – M-8888 – and I was on an Air Force flight to the wild blue yonder.

M-8888 was an easy and memorable number for my airmen and airwomen in the Air Force to remember. "Munda-8888" was the easy mail-call and easy lost-laundry call with a lost panty thrown in my face that had my "M-8888" scrawled on it in black on the waistband. You see, all military personnel have to put their coordinates on all their property including my all-cotton panties. Everyone knew me, and I knew everybody. Not because I was a red-state *Mary* or a blue-state *Eve*, but because I was from rural America and the Air Force was a happy step up for me socially and, most importantly, financially.

But for those girls coming from the blue-state coasts – being in the military was a step down. For some reason those blue-state babes in the military didn't have wealthy connections to businesses or opportunities back home. So, these blue-state sweat-hog women from inner cities and lez-be-frenz women from suburbia had to join the military. The majority of which is from southern red-state Appalachia. All of *Us* red-state and blue-state suckers are unlucky souls... we Americans (with our country two hundred and thirty-four (234) years old) still have to maybe die and kill for our food, clothing, and shelter. We have to kill in order to have a chance at getting out of poverty. We have to kill in order to live... and this makes me sad. Then it makes me very angry.

Didn't John Quincy Adams say, "I am a warrior, so my son will be a merchant, so that that his son may be a poet"?

Three generations into America in the mid-19th century, we did have America's best minds flower upon the world. Emerson, Whitman, Melville, Thoreau, and Wharton were the American Renaissance – the fruit of our American Revolution. The American Civil War happened on the heels of this New England Transcendentalism, but America has never regained that artistic drive ever again. And because in America, if you're not driving – you're dying, America rapidly devolved: artistically, literally, physically, and therefore, of course, metaphysically and spiritually.

And I am certainly no poet. I'm a rent-a-cop for Family Court, arresting polluted and perverted parents who abuse their children. And in a greater common sense or commonwealth sense or humanity sense – these pervs abuse OUR children. The New York Empire feudal system is thriving – because the Empire hates its children. I know this because my son and daughter are not educated to be poets. The Empire's educational system makes my children scared, jealous, and deranged. I didn't know this coming from West Virginia (WV) Appalachia. That's because in those smoky hills of America, whether for a woman or a man there: the multiple-choice life question on where you want to spend your life in Appalachia was not multiple-choice.

Appalachia is a duopoly from the start — am I going to jail today or am I not going to jail today. It is a prisoner's dilemma question couched unsuspiciously and unthreateningly as a harmless "Do you drive a Chevy or a Ford" question. Similar to the political, "Are you a Democratic or Republican?" question. All these life-choice questions are sold to *Us* as a multiple-choice question by *Them*.

But these multiple-choice questions are really duopoly questions in a two-party life, in our third-world West Virginia. Appalachian economics are a little Cournot, a little Bertrand, and together, a "Nash-Smash Equilibrium." In Appalachia, the cold duopoly is the coal mine or the military recruitment office between the online college and a sleazy pizza parlor. The *Nash-Smash Equilibrium* choice, the equilibrium of a country two hundred and thirty-four (234) years old for its children is: A: a life in a hole, or B: a life killing it. Life in America is sold as a zero-sum game, but it is really a non-zero-sum game — it is a minimax theorem. Life in America is a prisoner's question, not a women's question. American mothers and her children live within a prisoner's dilemma.

I chose to kill it but will never think of myself as a killer, a New Yorker, an empress, or part of the Empire. A bad marriage to a deadbeat Yankee, and then a divorce: me keeping the two children... stranded me here in New York State. I also realized the horrible education system in the rest of America and thought, "Why would I move from the Empire State?"

I need to persevere... My children, a ten (10) year-old boy emperor-in-training, and a twelve (12) year-old empress-in-training would take a serious educational, and more importantly, a social step down if we left the Empire. Sadly, I continued to meditate to myself... "If you cannot beat the Empire — join *Them*!" Morally, metaphysically, and on the right side of my brain I admit sadly to myself... *Constant Perseverance.*

Chapter 2

INTELLIGENCE

My muscled-up Ford Interceptor is running and humming along, fighting blue ridge highlands and plateau
valleys orientated in opposition to my east-to-west
travels. I smell and feel the flora flying by me.
Evergreen needles and conifers urgently talk to the
wide-leaved holly as if there has never been a spring
before. Red spruce and black spruce try to crowd out
the old favorite: the blue spruce. I'm hugging rid-
gelines and escarpments banking off the Kittatinny
Mountain Range and rolling on down to the Catskill
Delta. Coves of hemlock hang like dead men in pine
swamps as beavers smack their tails. The Eastern
Seaboard is in my rearview mirror and the heartland
of America is coming on fast. White-tailed deer in
my headlights stare at me like I'm the freak; skunks
caught in an eighteen (18) wheeler's way are pulver-
ized into *Nothing* but live on. The skunk lives on as
my car rolls over the *Pepé Le Pew* remains. "Ba-dump
— ba-dump," the skunk says, and I smell my compost-
ing future. This is the Eastern Continental Divide
of America. It gets quieter here... things slow down
here... I get nervous here... I like it here.

Following college graduation, I received a Reserve
Officer Training Corps (ROTC) commission from the

United State Air Force (USAF) at the West Virginia University (WVU). It was 1982, peacetime... and I enjoyed my work for six (6) years as an *Intelligence* Officer in Iran and Nicaragua. Six (6) years as a spy turned me onto knowledge (or supposed knowledge) as power. Power over mothers, power over motherly tribes, and power over motherly countries, power over mothers in order to manipulate her children. Fashion, language, video games, entertainment, and visual optics as coercion and manipulation. The mother's world is a simulacrum that *Them* created. And so, the military industrial complex only had to follow Plato's advice and brainwash all American mothers.

Plato said, *"Give me a different set of mothers and I will give you a different world."*

The active provocateur and/or *Intelligence* industry boiled it down for their own warmongering "Expectant-Mother-Racket" (EMR) and declared, "Change mothers, and we will change the world."

It wasn't just Telecommunications *Intelligence* (TELINT), Electronic (frequency) *Intelligence* (ELINT) or Human *Intelligence* (HUMTEL), but Psychological Operations (Psych-Ops) and Biological and Chemical Operations with the Department of Defense (DOD) and both the Federal Bureau of Investigation (FBI) and the Central *Intelligence* Agency (CIA). The target coordinate is the mother.

I was a Psychological Operations (Psych-Ops) mama in the Special Operations war in Nicaragua and Iran, but none of those places prepared me for the organized crime, the ongoing corruption and greed of the New York Empire State. The "Three-Men" oligarchs of Albany and its political corruption are worse than third-world countries with no sewer system, no school system, no clean water, and a millennium of tribal warfare.

But I knew what I was getting into because besides studying military sciences at West Virginia University, I studied philosophy and art history. Here in the right side of my brain, I meditate on *Intelligence,* which puts me light-years ahead of my rote peers in the Intelligence Community (IC).

Art history was incredible because history is taught not from war to war, or from banking-scam to banking-scam, but from art movement to art movement. Whether two-dimensional painting, sculpture, architecture, or literary works: our times and/or *Us* are judged not by our war scams, but by our art! My lucky peers in the art history world see life through rosy spectacles because life is all categorized chronologically by that great new painting, that incredibly designed building just constructed, or that intense new book with a new quirky prose, rhythm, and a very unique point of view (POV).

But being a military officer and constantly honored unnecessarily by the standing-army media, I thought incorrectly back in college that life was chronicled by our wars and banking scams that fund the wars. I thought life was on the left side of the brain with alphabets, numbers, and material goods, but I was wrong. The truth is life is Free-Grace – life is on the right side of the brain – life is but a dream.

Dear Family Court and Dear Reader, I don't want to solicit you, as I'm a student of Roger Williams, who, in 1649, as he was forming Providence, Rhode Island, declared: "Religion is the rape of the soul." But Free-Grace philosophy proposes we should care more about our spiritual goods than our material goods. There is some Free-Grace philosophy for you... and if you don't like these Socratic, Lutheran, and/or Anne Hutchinson thoughts, then please believe Bing Crosby's soulful and truthful voice when he sings the rhyme that stands the test of time:

"Row, row, row your boat – gently down the
stream.

Merrily, merrily, merrily – life is but a
dream."

The truth... with the mainstream media as a co-con-
spirator? Never! But an Albany Empire State forensic audit!? The *Upstate* Empire investigated as-is
by my still very active *Intelligence* Unit at Central
Command (CENTCOM) would indict and convict New York
legislatures and bureaucrats within days. The New
York Empire State Comptroller would be legally
crushed for what it punishes others in "Rogue" or
"Terrorist" countries for doing. The indictment for
crimes against humanity would fill up a squadron
of C-5 Galaxies. Explaining the extortion, bribery, self-dealing, and malfeasance of the New York
State legislature in US *Intelligence* standards to
the Unites State Congress would destroy the Empire.
Everyone, including the janitors in the Albany
State House, would be locked up in Leavenworth military correctional facilities for the rest of their
lives.

Albany capital region politicians are Banana-War
leftovers, these Albany Cavaliers and Courtiers
compared to the polite Contras, and the professional
Shia, is to say the least – embarrassing. But it is
dehumanizing as an American woman to play third-
world games in the capital of my American State.
I was a fan of "Free-market capitalism," "*Love*,"
and even *Motherhood* before my military time, but my
Intelligence experiences has taught me that those
things do not exist anymore.

I remember in the Markazi Province in Iran, 1985,
when a convoy of high-ranking local police we were
supporting came into our Forward Operating Location
(FOL) to buy some good old American weapons and
also give our *Intelligence* team some lame *Intel* on

the US embassy bombing in Beirut, Lebanon, that had
happened a couple years earlier.

Before any of these important subjects could be
discussed, there was first the matter of three (3)
Marines gang-raping and killing a young fourteen
(14) year old Arab girl a few weeks earlier in
Markazi. The question was whether the Marines would
be court-martialed in the US or tried in Iran under
Shia Islamic Law. The local police chief and/or the
"Supreme One" wanted the Marines castrated and crucified upside down as agents of the "Great Satan."
In opposition to these executions, my Intelligence
teammates were lobbying for some correctional
custody and definitely not three (3) upside-down
crosses on a Middle Eastern desert hill. I think
we've all seen that three (3) cross picture before,
and this Markazi police chief was an old "Friend"
of *Intelligence* - so he was taunting *Us*.

In order to have the chief of police see a resurrection in retribution, he accepted ten (10) trac-
tor-trailer trucks with American weapons and four
(4) stainless-steel suitcases filled with American
cash. The cash was being delivered by four (4)
dancing-boys in women's colorful miniskirts and
what looked like Coca-Cola T-shirts. But instead
of "Enjoy Coca-Cola" written out in that smooth
and sexy white script on a red background, the text
said, "Enjoy Baca-Bazi" / *Enjoy boy-play*.

Some jesters on the Intel or Special Operations
team had capsulized our American foreign policy in
this very picture I'm drawing for you. In this picture, besides the four (4) tortured boys grimacing
in pain holding upwards of four million dollars
($4,000,000) cash, there were four (4) mothers, or
what I believe to be four (4) mothers, in head-to-
toe black burqas. The dusty burqas only had embroi-
dered eyes-holes, so whoever was in there could
see. The Arab pervert men seem to think sexual

assault and rape of children is okay if their mothers deliver the boys graciously.

One of the mothers and/or black-moving-blankets in
Arabic said, "Thank you, Supreme One, for making *Us*
so worthy to allow our sons to serve you tea and
dance for your holiness. They also have a special
lotion for that toothache we know you have, and
they alone will liberally soothe that ache. Thank
you, Supreme One, thank you."

The Arab police officer thanked the black-moving-
blankets, and then the black-moving-blankets thanked
Them some more. This picture... of these four (4)
mothers giving away their Coca-Cola dancing-boys to
a pervert in a foreign, ill-fitting military officer's clown outfit hurts me to this day.

And it's not the four million dollars ($4,000,000,000)
of United States tax dollars that angers me. It's
the known-unknown. It's that when the US. sells
"Freedom, democracy, and Coca-Cola," what they're
really selling is a slow-motion rape, murder, dis-
section, and autopsy of your children.

Which visually brings me to the other horrible
part of my Coca-Cola military career, which was in
1987. It was in Managua, Nicaragua, where I again
saw those satirical "Enjoy Coca-Cola" T-shirts some
joker had made up. But here in Nicaragua, the white
stylish script on the bold red background said,
"Enjoy Crack." The shirts were on children and
teenager cocoa-pickers in the Nicaraguan jungle.
The kids were all orphans and addicted to the cocoa
plant, as you could tell by their erratic behavior
and their dirty, decadent demeanor. They would also
constantly sniffle with runny noses, and then there
were their eyes... their dead, dark eyes like those
of toothless sharks in a foul and murky aquarium.
The cocaine the children were harvesting was being
sent up to South Central Los Angeles as "Crack."
These young slaves seemed to be making the best of

their drug-slave life, but one tough girl tried to make friends with me, unfortunately.

Her name was Lupe, and she told me a story about a family of monkeys nearby in the jungle. In the shanties where the children workers slept, the monkeys would come around and scavenge all the crap American fast-food we were bringing in from the US. Lupe was feeding the monkeys her scraps, but because the monkeys are all cocaine fiends, the monkeys got hostile when not fed enough. At first, the monkeys would only pull Lupe's hair, screech, or scratch her for more Coca-Cola straight from American *Intelligence* budgets.

But Lupe with a Spanish accent said, "Monkeys are like my jefe / *boss*. I hate my jefe, so I started to throw rocks at the monkeys last month, but then the monkeys started throwing rocks at me." Lupe had a large black eye and said that three (3) days ago, she got hit by a large rock thrown by a small, ratty monkey. Lupe continued, "I haven't been able to go out of the dorms for almost a month. So, I asked my boyfriend, Carlos, who is a Contra soldier, to start shooting the monkeys."

Lupe's hands were shaking as she was wringing them like an eighty (80) year-old spinster with dementia harping about an inheritance she didn't receive to her lawyer who is overcharging her. Lupe said, "The monkeys were baited by Carlos and his friends, and then they started shooting. The monkey's brains were being splattered across the jungle, and the monkeys still came back for the American Ding Dong treats with only half a brain in their skull."

Lupe started to ponder something important in her mind and seemed to gain the strength to say it, but a trickle of red blood slowly came from her nose and dripped into her small mouth. Lupe got embarrassed. After wiping her nose on her dirty flannel she wore over her "Enjoy Crack" shirt, Lupe said,

"I was thinking of asking Carlos to shoot me...
Us... the real stupid monkeys here in the jungle."

I said, "What are talking about? You're working for
freedom and democracy, and for a new, good government. The Sandinistas are bad commies." As I said
these last lame words, I started to cringe because
I knew this very smart child was gonna see through
my bullshit.

Lupe scoffed immediately and got up with a pissy
attitude because she realized she wouldn't get the
truth from me, *Intelligence*, and/or *Them*.

Lupe laughed in my face and started to walk away.
She looked back and concluded as she wiped her nose
again with the end of her dirty flannel shirt sleeve
and spit into the voracious green jungle. She then
declared, overemphasizing some words, "There is no
such thing as good government. You just **get it**...
while **the gettin's good!**"

Capitalism in 2021 is dead. *Motherhood* in 2021
is dead. Motherly "*Love*" is proud mothers delivering their boy-toy sons to debt, poverty, and
pedophiles. Motherly *Love* is suitcases filled with
friendly-fire cash in the light of day. The corruption of the Contras in Nicaragua, the Shia in Iran,
or the politicians in Albany are based on extortion
and/or bribery of the mother. These third-world
politics and accounting books will look identical to the historians and anthropologists that dig
through our ashes.

The loyalist-royalist politicians of the Empire
don't let the ball drop as the shell game goes around
and around in circles of *Intelligence*, counterin-
telligence, and counterinsurgent *Intelligence*. The
Empire State's "Law" now declares that "An official
act" of a politician may be bribery... the Empire
Law and the *Law* of the land now declares that bribery is not bribery. The *Law* and the Federal Court

Judge apologizes to the Defense and says "Collusion is no longer collusion, and racketeering is no longer racketeering in the Empire State of America. You are free to go. The Court apologizes and will gladly sanction the prosecutors and District Attorneys who questioned your 'Official acts.'" The preference for the Empire courtier or Cavalier to underestimate criminal factors and overestimate their own importance is an illusory correlation. This is a Psych-Ops *coup d'état* on the evolutionary matrix for capitalist correlation.

Evidence for crimes against the citizen, or *Motherhood,* will bring a judgment. But through Appeals, Acquittals, and media subversion. The Empire's criminals will keep mothers' preference for corruption in place. The persistence of an oligarchy in the Albany Empire State is the preference of loyalist-royalists to keep the time-tested leverage of a prison-ship incarceration always floating nearby. The child, the citizen, and/or the mother in the Empire is the "Real,*" and *Motherhood* becomes the *little-Object-A.* The secondary "Other" is the mother as a political force – which is the enemy of war. The mother and female citizen is forgotten on purpose and outsourced to a weaker mother from a recent-immigration demographic or war refugees from our latest "Freedom and Democracy War." Without evidence from a forensic audit, and without Commonwealth citizens, the Judgment and Democracy never comes to the Empire State. And that's how the child-abusing mothers have designed it.

This Empire State's citizen-craft, similar to priest-craft, mother-craft, and king-craft, is the bone marrow of capitalism, patriarchy, and war. Sun Tzu was right about a lot of things with war, but I think he forgot that war starts with *Motherhood* and/or mothers who will allow their creation – their child – to be killed for cash. Capitalism, Judeo-Christian psychological debt, and *Motherhood* form the triple helix of war.

Similar to a man-of-war jellyfish, women within patriarchal societies are the mother-of-war. We are transparent, have no propulsion of our own, and we float with a sail of hot gas. Our lives depend on the winds and tides within the Empire. With mother-craft tentacles one hundred (100) feet long, we fish, penetrate, and poison all who are hostile to *Us* and our fashionable survival. With a blue cloak and a mauve dagger, we network with friendlies and the unfriendly. We disrupt everything and neutralize everyone in nontraditional ways that sharpen our trade-craft or mother-craft. Whether alive, dead, or dismembered, we can sting and paralyze our prey – we are carnivores, we are man-eaters, and we create an open sky of *Motherhood*.

As a jellyfish mother, we have official cover (OC), but as a motherless bitch or lesbian, we have Non-Official Cover (NOC), so we are handled by motherly handlers. *Mary* is a handler, but she is a double-agent and spies on *Eve,* another mother handler for the Federal Bureau of Investigation (FBI) and the Central *Intelligence* Agency's (CIA) gaze. For the cockroach's gaze.

The cutouts within the *Intelligence* lexicon are the Israeli arms dealer selling missiles to the Contras, or perhaps an El Salvadorian MS-13 crack dealer in Los Angeles selling cocaine to African Americans. The military *Intelligence* community I was with in 1986 was worlds away from that CIA, but that didn't stop those *Intel* peers of mine from working with Central American and Middle Eastern death-squads dealing drugs in LA and dealing arms in Jerusalem.

These third-world death-squads are now Incorporated (INC) as the police and/or pharmaceutical companies, and they rule the Empire. They are not just killing citizens; more profitable is the addicting and incarcerating of their people with biological and chemical (BC) warfare. BC operations includes

Genetically Modified Organisms (GMO) in all food and
water sources ingested by all Americans, biological and chemical operational agents in all pharmaceuticals on the "White-Market" including opioids,
depressants, mood-altering drugs, and pain reliev-
ers. BC agents are also spread with more operational
experimentation in all "Black Market" pharmaceuticals including crack, heroin, methamphetamines,
MDMA, and all strains of cannabis sativa. This perpetual state of soft-core war and/or "Drug War,"
this eternal state of addiction and incarceration
with biological and chemical agents, is hardest for
the mother and child. Within the Empire, *Motherhood*
has been redacted from civilization. Some men, bar-
barians, and animal-like men thrive in this kill-
or-be-killed world. For me: the militaristic life
or the "Danger-Close" life was what I had to do to
get out of poverty and Appalachia in West Virginia.
Unlike the majority of veterans, the military for
me was a stepping stone, not a foundation.

Regardless, militaristic senators and legislators
of the Empire ham it up with third-world death-squads
at graduation ceremonies at the United States (US)
Special Warfare Center and School (SWCS). These
Central American pirates, Middle Eastern pirates,
and any international pirates with a pulse and
pockets to be filled up with American dollars. They
say "In God We Trust" and are given a full military
parade welcoming *Them* to American military bases
and/or "WARS R US." Death-squads and drug-deal-
ers need to stay up to date on warfare technology,
and America is the warfare convention that doesn't
end. With American money, these mercenaries didn't
just rig the voting back in Central America and the
Middle East — they strafed and salted the earth
with American-made weapons and mines before, after,
and during the vote on Election Day.

And unfortunately, I helped by delivering
"*Intelligence*" and/or suitcases of American tax
money to the tribe of the day within the third-world

city of the month. Was it the Pequot or Palestinian tribe that got the suitcase and boy-toy yesterday? Regardless, mothers would give their son or daughter (sometimes as young as ten (10) years old) to me, so in turn I gave *Them* to pedophiles and perverts. I gave *Them* to *Them*....

Today, maybe the Seneca or Shia tribes will be visited by Santa Claus, the American pervert? These tribes can sit on Santa's lap, and they can talk about what they want and then, magically, they get what they asked for. But only if they were good and continue to: "In God We Trust."

And now is this espionage or extortion? Is this *Intelligence* or babysitting? I feel more like a crossing guard with a gun than a military officer with a master's degree. Our American foreign policy is nothing more than enabling a "Fight Club" in order to see who the "Winner" is and, therefore, who the US will bank-roll. Divide and Conquer 101.

Thankfully, back at the West Virginia University (WVU), I also took a lot of philosophy and literature courses, which also enhanced my *Intelligence*. Whether it's the Sumerians, the Hermetics, Seneca, Cato, the Gnostics, Kant, Nietzsche, Sartre, Foucault, or Lacan: I know - I know. And these great thinkers allow me to calm down; they allow me to stay out of the right-side-brain rut.

There were also my literary anchors of Appalachia - my bibles. First and foremost is Faulkner with plenty of *Mother's Day Madness* in "As I Lay Dying." Then there is Steinbeck's "*Of Mice and Men*" because Lenny and George's dream and goal of a self-sufficient farm is an Appalachian dream. When Lenny wants to hear about "The rabbits," he is told a placating Appalachian myth and a delusionary tale that is told every night in Appalachia to every hopeful Appalachian child.

Mom, dad, bro, grandma, or sis in Appalachia says, "Yes, I will read you a bedtime story about the rabbits and the farm we're gonna buy." But this sweet dream turns into an Appalachian nightmare because it is not supportive, inspirational, or *Intelligence*. It's a forewarning fable: the good future with rabbits on a profitable farm is an Appalachian Holy Grail never found.

And rounding out my Appalachian *Intelligence* is, of course, "<u>Good Country People</u>" by Flannery O'Connor.

Please, Family Court and Dear Reader, I don't want to spoil a good read, so like a good teacher, I'll let you do your own reading homework with "Dewey Dell," "Lenny," and "Hulga," for here is the unsaid of Appalachia – here is the Commandments of Chattanooga. So, while you read this deposition here, you may see those Appalachian characters because they are all here, along with many more.

This motherly *Intelligence* comes with a price and debt. I'm not a mother, I'm a standing-army mother. There is no comparison.

And this mommy-debt comes from unknown lenders, aka "The Federal Reserve." The mommy-debtor's life we have led in Appalachia and America for the last ten (10) years (since 2011) is a credit card cash advance we cannot afford. It's an "Armageddon Now" credit card, it's a "Resurrection Ready Re-fi," it's an "Apocalyptic Equity Line." *Nothing* in that Zion agenda or budget is for the non-Judeo-Christian... but the Special Warfare School gets four hundred and fifty-eight million dollars ($458,000,000) to host international cutthroats and their scumbag handlers.

Our American financial debt is around thirty-one trillion dollars ($31,000,000,000,000) here in 2021, and the moral hazard interest rate and the guilt of the American mother will rise alongside that Armageddon debt. The more a derelict mother breeds into civilization instead of fixing her civilization, the more femininity is destroyed. The wise-owl mother owl does not breed unless her hunting is successful. Why am I and all mothers stupider than a night bird?

For the standing-army mother within the Empire, the best deception is self-deception. Coded mistakes give *Motherhood* authenticity as imperial *Intelligence* (IMINT). The patriotic mother that gives up her children to be abused and killed is not a mother, but a third-world whore. The American whore-mother only exists in a safe house or near a military base. Motherly spooks use cryptanalysis and networks of agents to influence *Motherhood.* The mommy networks use propaganda, deception, and support only friendly forces.

The changing nature and threat to the "Truth" and counterdeception *Intelligence* for the *truth* begs the question — what is motherly *Intelligence?* What is motherly deception? What is motherly espionage? Is this again... a woman question: what is the woman's purpose in life? Is our mother-craft, our *Motherhood,* a false-flag, an agent provocateur? Is this covert and overt *Intelligence* question a deceptive question? Is our counterinsurgency *Intelligence* feeding off of *Us,* the motherly host? Is this a *Red-Queen* question or a woman question? Was my grandmother right that *Motherhood* is a man-made invention?

The Empire and their third-world media in San Salvador, Kabul, and Appalachia always block the "Truth" and control the *truth.* Before the drumbeat of war is even heard in the Empire, the Empire manufactures false truths for the mother first. The Empire assassinates *Motherhood* first because without willing soldiers and the patriotic mothers that birth and brainwash *Them*, there would be no war.

Family Court and Good Reader, please believe me
this is child abuse, and our standing-army for a
foreign Empire will be outlawed again one day in
America – as it was from 1787-1906.

Until then, this wet affair / this child abuse is
when a woman's and a mother's liberation is sab-
otaged, neutralized, and destroyed. My own soul's
moral hazard, with my military excuse to get out of
poverty by joining the United States (US) standing-army killing machine, was ignoble and dirty.
Killing destroys my *Nothing,* my subconsciousness.
Killing becomes a God over the silence. I, as a
militaristic woman for a standing-army am no asset;
I am a handmaid sow – I am a liability with no value
and easily replaced. In 2021, as a veteran officer
of the Air Force, I barely still have enough food,
clothing, and shelter for me and my family. And like
Motherhood and the citizens with me in the Empire —
we are not honorable. As feminine moles, defectors,
and traitors, we have perverted Sun Tzu's "The Art
of War," into "The Art of Child Abuse."

So, like Sun Tzu and his Machiavellian mothers with
no respect for themselves or those they give birth
to, we spy and exploit our neighbors and our children. I'm your intelligent mother, I'm your fascist
government, and I read your mail! For myself, the
mother, or citizen of this Abrahamic Empire, our
only feminist tool is loyalty, so our only weapon
is treason and disloyalty. I am a citizen and a
mother in the Empire – I am a spook, I am a ghost,
I am dishonorable. I am neither Mary, Marianne, nor
Eve. I am the "*Other,*" living in a man's world or
a cockroach's fearful imagination. I am a wannabe
mother / a wannabe heroine, but I'm trapped within
a cockroach's gaze. I am lonely... I am not living
– I am acting against my own feminine interests. My
Sister X gene unravels me and my spirit as I get
older, and it's harder to keep the feminine façade
up. I play a part; I am a Divine drone, homing in
on a motherly kill... just killing it.

My cryptology *Intelligence* in Central America and in the Middle East employed not just the target, the target's friends and family, but the target's honeypot, their mailman, their drug dealer, and their maid. And that electric utility worker and landscaping worker just outside their home is *Intelligence*. My crypto-*Intel* is no different with my work for the Child Protective Services (CPS), as it employs all those entities and much more *Intel*. But let *Us* not forget the spook's motto:

"Those that Findeth *Intel* – Will Loseth *Intel*."

I decided to investigate both child-abuse Complaints (#21-4532 and #21-6154) at the same time on Mother's Day. The target child or target family is best reviewed on the day of rest, plus I like clocking the overtime (OT). As usual, I coordinated numerous public and "Private" *Intel* investigations before my surveillance today.

All elementary and high-school report cards for the possibly abused children are in their files and come via their schools. The parents' and grandparents' Department of Motor Vehicles (DMV) records are filed alphabetically, as well as their State and Federal Tax Department records for the last ten (10) years. The parents' Allegheny police department records, the last five (5) years of bank records, their employment records, their health records, their credit reports, their social media accounts, and their cell-station transcripts for the last month have been reviewed and are all filed alphabetically in a cascade mode on my laptop. All this *Intel* coupled with some old spy tricks and some new Stingray eyes and ears surveillance equipment allows me to be the *"Connie Bond"* of Child Protective Services (CPS). This *Intelligence* data will be assess two (2) different families, six (6) children at polar ends of the Allegheny socioeconomic scale representing possible child abuse in poverty and possible child abuse in luxury. The anonymous allegations of abuse

have the common denominator that the mother is
the abusive parent. This deposition with numerical
dictation as well as the customary Public Exhibit
illustrations and paintings will be filed with this
New York State Family Court in Allegheny County.

1
2
3
4
5
6
7
8
9
10
11
12
13
14
15
16
17
18
19
20
21
22
23
24
25
26
27
28
29
30
31
32
33
34
35
36
37
38
39
40
41
42

Chapter 3

MR. APPLETON

1 "Allegheny is a little north of the Catskills, a
2 little south of Syracuse, and further west than
3 California," as told to me earlier on Friday morning
4 before I left Albany by my boss, Mr. Appleton. Mr.
5 Appleton is a rotund, cuddly, sad man. Mr. Abraham
6 Appleton looks and acts like a weak-kneed and plump
7 Abe Lincoln. He was sassy for a Midwestern veteran,
8 but Mr. Appleton is mostly an "Angry-Librarian," an
9 Albany bureaucrat, a eunuch employee of the Empire
10 – *Real*, but not ideal.
11
12 Mr. "A" or Abe are nicknames that give Mr. Appleton
13 a thrilling rush. His nicknames allowed Abe the
14 *Angry-Librarian* (AL) to live within his library as
15 a character instead of an employee. Reality makes
16 Abe indignant. Within digital numbers, Abe cate-
17 gorized and filed everything not with the Dewey
18 Decimal System, but with his own emotional gooey
19 jelly-roll system. His analogue system makes him
20 feel at home with furry slippers, plaid pajamas,
21 and cheese-doodle ice cream in his moldy base-
22 ment. His basement is paneled meticulously with
23 five (5) different types of brown faux-wood panel-
24 ing and is carpeted wall-to-wall in light green.
25 Mr. Appleton's "Aka" allowed him to live as if

he were dangerous, a Moog synthesis living up to
his name of Abraham Appleton. I usually got Abe's
furry eyebrows to stand up on end by calling him my
"Abe-Babe," which, unbeknownst to Abraham, really
brought out his *Upstate* transgender dreams.

I said in a sedate, airless voice, just like every
morning at 7:25 a.m. for the last eight (8) years,
walking into Mr. Appleton's office, as he stares
out his windows waiting for the sun to shine, "Good
morning, Mr. Appleton."

The problem with waiting for the sun in the "Capital
Region" in America is that the sun does not show
up. Nor does it rain when it rains. In all Capital
Towns across America the only weather report is
which way the money is blowing. Within the Empire
State's Capital Region, it blows north by northeast, hard and continuously up the Hudson River.
Weather in the *Capital Regions*, like weather in all
Capital Towns – is not experienced; it only creates
clouds of political and financial opportunities
when there are really none.

Mr. Appleton looked around, bright-eyed and bushy-
tailed, and sang as usual, "Good morning, Connie!"
Then Mr. Appleton, as he did every day, took on an
air of Empire importance and authority and pre-
tended to distribute the Empire's wealth, exclaiming, "One (1) for you; six (6) for me. One half
(1/2) for you; twelve (12) for me. One quarter
(1/4) for you; twenty-four (24) for me."

Mr. Appleton laughed heartily at his own daily
joke, laughing at himself more than others. This
tragic comedy was Mr. Appleton's yoga. The Empire's
"Oooommm" mantra was the rope that was strangling /
hanging Abe, the twenty million (20,000,000) resi-
dents of the Empire State, and the three hundred and
twenty million (320,000,000) citizens of America.

Mr. Appleton's Empire joke that always started our

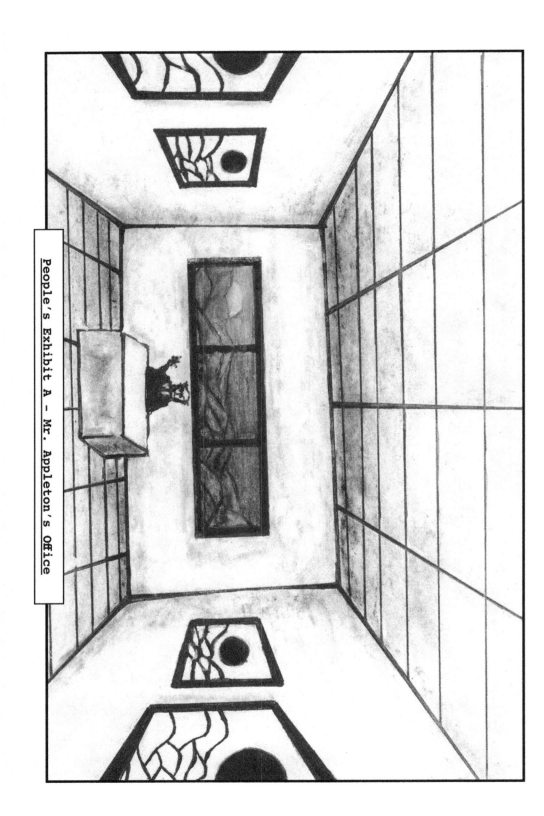

People's Exhibit A – Mr. Appleton's Office

mornings was delivered in order to ground *Us* and/
or check and balance *Us* at Child Protective Service
(CPS) officers in order to understand where we were
and what we were doing within the Albany bowels of
the Empire. I enjoyed eating this shit for breakfast because it allowed me to look forward to the
rest of the day, and Mr. Appleton (also a military
veteran) understood this prosperity consciousness.

Abraham Appleton sported a trim auburn beard around
his jawbone that encircled his fat head. His eyes
were lost and wondering. He celebrated bureaucracy
with a huge ass - one assumed to show off his unsaid
Empirical power within this fat-ass Empire State.
Abe's ass was legendary within the brute, cold-war
concrete of Albany architecture. Like all good families, comrades, patriots, and friends within the
"Community" of an Empire that are brutish bullies,
your "Friends" and "Family" are betting on your
demise. Likewise, citizens of northern Appalachia
/ these rowdy Yankees within the Empire would take
bets on Mr. Appleton's buttocks' seasonal width
and its winter weight. At least back home in West
Virginia and down south, people cut you down from
behind, but up north here — these Yankees cut you
down laughing in your face. Mr. Appleton's fat ass
and its algorithmic future girth was wagered on
incessantly in many Albany break rooms, in numerous
Empire State boiler rooms, in many seedy American
Legions, and in a few lonely Adirondack dive bars
with neon signs and Mohawk Indian ghosts still
stalking the white man in the dark spots of the
parking lot filled with pick-up trucks. The ass
bets and ass pools happened because Mr. Appleton was
an asshole that could take the hits. Mr. Appleton
enjoyed being an asshole - he was conceived to be
an asshole. He definitely was not the *Red-Queen*'s
sexy-son, but her louse, her awkward numb-nut.
And the "Ass" betting pools will continue, as the
Capital Region eunuchs need a piñata to bat around.

And it wasn't because Mr. Appleton had frequent

lunches with the infamous Empire royal fascists
known as "Three (3) Men in a Room." *Three (3)
Men in a Room* were Governor Amato from Queens,
Long Island; Speaker of the House Assembly Silver
from the Lower East Side (LES) of Manhattan; and
Majority Leader Skelos from Nassau, Long Island. It
wasn't that Appleton was the fourth (4th) man in this
room for the Empire... as a "Catering-Consultant"
to bring in bags of breakfast sandwiches, lavish
lunch hoagies, and fine-dining deli-runs... And it
wasn't because he had the nicest office within New
York State's double-dipping nirvana. And it wasn't
because Mr. Appleton was on the State Assembly
budget committee, otherwise known in Albany as
the "Staten Island Math Club" or "Speaker Silver
Enterprises."

Chapter 4

THREE MEN IN A ROMAN CIRCLE JERK

Mr. Appleton questioned me, "So, you know, Munda, that this Empire joke isn't a joke? You know this *Three (3) Men in a Room* 'Down-Stater' bullshit (BS) allows all of *Us Upstate* Democrats, Republicans, Progressives, Independents, and even the dande- lions to feel clean and politically correct in continuing the four-hundred (400) year-old North Country or *Upstate* tradition of calling all New York City downstaters 'Scumbags.' And so *Up-State* doesn't care because we're a charity case / a 'Write-Off' for 'Wall Street's' financial crimes, for Madison Avenue's social manipulation, and for Fashion Avenue's clown outfits we have to wear and pay too much for.

"Now you see, Munda." Mr. Appleton addresses me by my last name (even though I outrank him militarily) not as an insult, but for veterans, addressing one another with our last names (officer or enlisted) is endearing, for a soldier's life shared. It is camaraderie and/or *esprit de corps* for an eternal warrior bond.

Appleton continued, "The Empire's *Upstaters* – *Us* – and her dandelions are partly right. If you are

a New York citizen and have felt left out of the
Empire State's growth since 1994, it's not because
you're losing it, not working hard enough, or feel
inadequate and left behind. No, absolutely not,
because if you're not a crook or connected to a
crook in New York... you feel out of place... left
out of the game."

Appleton elaborated, "The Empire State's citizen-
ship / like *Motherhood* has been hijacked and sold
out to the refugee and/or immigrant tribe of the
week. And all this with television (TV) financing
available, car financing available, and lots of
credit card (CC) financing available. TVs, cars,
and credit cards are freedom! The Empire's one-hun-
dred-and-fifty-billion-dollar($150,000,000,000)
budget is at stake and fortunes are made every year
with the *Three (3) Men in a Room* governance known
as 'New York politics or a Roman Circle Jerk.'"

Appleton explained, "Now you see, Munda, Child
Protective Services (CPS), *Motherhood,* and/ or
child abuse did not make it onto the New York State
Budget with Cuomo, Silver, and Skelos. Those three
(3) men were otherwise known as Vinny, Vinny, and
Vinny in the Albany Capital Region because they ran
their fraudulent pizza-parlor front so damn well."

I replied, "Pizza-parlor front?"

And Appleton rebutted, "Oh, sorry, you're not from
New York. I call 'The New York State House' a
pizza-parlor front, like those old Little Italy,
NYC mob-fronts where you could get a loan, make a
bet, get some great garlic knots, pay for a hit,
get a greasy slice to-go, and/or get a quickie...."
Appleton paused a moment for effect and then said,
"Albany's State House is no better."

Mr. Appleton wondered, "Now I don't know what will
become of these sexual allegations by numerous women
against Governor Cuomo, who, as you know, has gone

to great lengths to prove himself not a homo. And his machismo was always so forced, so blatant and bizarre, that it became an ongoing Albany Empire joke. But why would a Senator's son act like he wanted to get caught?"

Appleton continued, "But you know, Munda, let me say, if it sounds like a joke — it is a joke. Now Albany and her fine people are no joke. And all New Yorkers from Chautauqua Lake to Montauk Lake are not a joke, and certainly all Americans from sea to shining sea are not a joke. But as I said, Munda, you know, following the ducky quack-quack analogy: if it sounds and walks like a joke - it is a joke."

Appleton reminisces, "So, when I start introducing Three (3) Men in a Room Empire politics and say, 'So, two Italians and a Jew walk into a bar' - see right there - it's a joke already. Please remember those 1970s and 1980s racist joke books by Larry Wilde. They checked and balanced every known demographic to America at the time. One part 'National Lampoon's' another part 'MAD' and it skewered, devolved, and crushed racism with comedy into the tragic democracy that is our American life."

Appleton concluded, "So anyway, two Italians and a Jew from New York City walk into a bar to spend one hundred and fifty billion ($150,000,000,000) dollars within an Empire year. I'm wondering Connie, now listen to me... do I even need a punch line?"

Mr. Appleton whirled around from his big office windows and said, "What is that old saying about Empire politics? 'Within the Empire, the more friends you make today - the more enemies you'll have tomorrow.'"

Appleton, getting lawyerly says, "But Speaker Silver was arrested in 2015 for extortion and bribery, and luckily his lawyer-politician criminal friends Cuomo, Silver, and Skelos previously had set up more 'Laws' in order to allow all these Empire crooks to get off on legal technicalities."

Appleton walks up to me and puts his hand on my shoulder and looks me in the eye to drive home his point, "The military's forensic audit that is fast approaching Albany, and all immoral Empires, will make El Salvador and Iraq accounting look like economic angels compared to the New York Legislature's malfeasance, extortion, bribery, and crimes against humanity."

I spoke up and said, "Isn't the Silver political rule the golden rule?"

Mr. Appleton, my teacher / my boss / my drill sergeant, said, "No, Munda, and I know you know this, so don't play cute. The Silver Law wouldn't work in a military court because the *DOD* doesn't listen to third-world answers from Americans accused of treason pleading, 'Well, that is how we do business in Albany.'"

Appleton dialed down, "'That is how we do business' is NOT accepted in El Salvador or Iraq, but it's accepted here in Albany as a legal answer. And it's accepted in Washington, DC, as a legal answer. And unbelievably *That is how we do business* – is accepted at the United States Supreme Court (USSC) as a legal answer."

Appleton again reminisces, "Don't you remember, Munda, at that press conference in 2017 or 2018, I forget, but the NY Attorney General (AG) Preet Bharara had an earful for New York and New Yorkers the day after his office indicted two (2) of the three (3) men in the Empire room – Silver and Skelos."

Appleton, animated now, delights in telling this story, "So, Mr. Bharara, with tongue firmly in cheek, asked New Yorkers at his presser a very good question, to which he never got an answer. 'There are by my count 213 men and women in the New York State legislature, and yet it is common knowledge that only three men essentially wield all the power.' Bharara turned the knife, laughing at all of New York and her pathetic subjects. 'I must confess a little bit of confusion about this because I'm from India: When did this come to pass? Why has everyone just come to accept it? When did twenty million (20,000,000) New Yorkers agree to be ruled like a triumvirate in Roman times?'"

Appleton laughed triumphantly and roared, "I know who Caesar is, but, Munda, here is a question for you and your *Intelligence* friends: 'Who is Brutus?'"

Mr. Appleton spoke like Cato the Younger and boasted, "I can hear the historians and accountants twenty (20) years from now, Munda... laughing at *Us*, then again fifty (50) years from now, one hundred (100) years from now in 2121! These laughing historians and anthropologists then will be asking themselves, 'What was wrong with those New Yorkers from 1995–2015 to let those atrocities happen with their money, within their State?' A focused photograph framed in dark expensive walnut will be held up as 'Exhibit Q.'"

Appleton turned lawyerly and spoke like a good storyteller: "Now please listen intently: In this framed photograph, the *Three (3) Men in a Room* of the New York State House are not in a room discussing the Empire's budget, but they are having a hell of a good time in the Hamptons on Long Island. The picture is at the exclusive Southampton Bath and Tennis Club on Gin Lane. They are all wearing the fashion of preppy college boys from New England on Cape Cod, but they are all grotesquely out of shape and look like hairy, grinning, perverted apes. The punch line of the Empire's *Three (3) Men in a Room* government is embossed in brass on the bottom of the photograph's frame. It reads in bold capitals,

'MISTRIAL.' This Empire trophy picture might answer some questions for those anthropologists in 2121 interested in looking back at 2021 and studying the old Empire's control-frauds and psychological operations." Appleton, getting tired, concludes in a downbeat tone and with an Appalachian twang: "And you know, Munda, hindsight is always twenty / twenty (20/20)."

I said, "Well, Mr. Appleton, isn't this an attorney general (AG) question? A Department of Justice (DOJ) question? An Empire State citizen question? Or at least a mother question - a woman question?"

Mr. Appleton replied, "Listen, Munda, I don't know what type of question it is, but the answer to my imaginative 'What was wrong with those New Yorkers?' question has no intelligent answer. An *Intelligence* answer, an empirical answer, and/or a moral answer is not a clean answer. We can ask my imaginative 'Downstate' friends Vinny, Vinny, and Vinny for an honest answer. But there's no answer, because there is no question that New York City scumbags are NOT cowards and crooks."

Appleton dug in and became dark: "All you have to do is look back in horror at the New York Draft Riots in 1860 or the Brooklyn prison ships during the American Revolution from 1776-1783. Remember, Munda, 'Downstate' New Yorkers are the scumbag's scumbag — with only New York scumbag values. Let *Us* not forget in 1776 that these New York loyalists to royalty helped the British chase away George Washington and then tortured and killed eleven thousand (11,000) American men in the first ever concentration camp or death camp ever run during modern times. New Yorkers killed more American patriots on those Brooklyn prison ships than the English army killed on all American battlefields combined."

Appleton continued, "A 'Downstate' New Yorker is a

royalist / loyalist who doesn't sleep and will kill for fashion, money, and/or capital. The descendants and heirs of those loyalist lawyers and prison guards from those Brooklyn prison ships watched the World Trade Center implode in 2001 and actually wondered aloud, 'Why *Us*?' These loyalist / royalist New Yorkers chalked up another three thousand (3,000) American patriots and/or victims who died for the Empire's good, and not New York's good, and especially not America's good."

Mr. Appleton concluded, "With regards to your parental abuse question, the dumbed-down question is, 'What was wrong with those Empire mothers?' The answer, then and now - and you know this, being a great Child Protective Services (CPS) officer - is that loyalist-royalist mothers will imprison their children and each other. They will kill their children and each other to get ahead in the Empire."

Mr. Appleton fell into a sad silence very far away... It lasted too long, but I didn't know what to say. I thought sadly and silently. I didn't agree with him out loud because it would have been too insulting to so many mothers and women in the many Empires and wannabe Empires around the world.

I shuffled my feet, swallowed hard, and said, "Well, we all try." As I said the words, a silent and vivid slideshow of every mean, cunty, and nasty New York woman I've ever met came across my mind. And please excuse me, Honorable Family Court and Good Reader, but we all know the mean girls from New York.

Dear Family Court and Good Reader, let's please agree that language is fluid and evolving. Let us look at language for a moment. The United Kingdom (UK) English vernacular is over one thousand and five hundred (1,500) years old and has many dialects dependent upon the UK colony's location. Our United States (US) English vernacular is only two hundred and thirty-four (234) years old and has room for improvement. Therefore, I declare here and now in this deposition for *Us to* follow the British's (*Them*) linguistic lead and liberally call "Cunts" a *Cunt.* Yes, that dreaded word that American women are still too coy and prude to use – *Cunt.* It feels so good when I say it in my throat and on my tongue. And why not? What's wrong with using slang for my pussy? What's wrong with a clean cat in a well-organized and tidy barn? Hell... I'm talking to you from my pussy right now.

Mr. Appleton dismisses me with a trailing one-word question: "Try?"

Yet, United States (US) women with their last two hundred and thirty-four (234) years of Independence still cannot grow a pair of ovaries and call *Red-Queen* women *Cunts....*

In the United Kingdom (UK), a big-mama female hooligan footballer from Manchester will use the word *Cunt* just as much as an American female rapper from the Bronx, New York, uses the word *Fuck.*

The Manchester mum will call everyone *a cunt,* from her own mother to the bartender at her pub, to the late-night shag she taunts at dawn merrily with, "I'll see later, you little limp-dick cunt."

And Dear Family Court and Good Reader, please bear with me, and as a tangent to this cunt propaganda, can I please ask why Americans have a negative connotation towards "Fucking?" To sex? To erotica? It's not just New Yorkers who use the word "Fuck" way too much and in a negative connotation. We say, "Why the fuck?" and "Who the fuck?" and "Don't get fucked!" and "Let's get fucked up!" Americans talk about making *love* like it's a war, a sexually transmitted disease (STD) and/or a crime.

So, Honorable Family Court and Dear Reader, in the spirit of evolving the American women's vernacular and intellect, I will use the word *Cunt* a lot more in this Family Court deposition. You know the Empire *Cunt* I'm talking about – you know the New Yorker *Cunt* we all hate but emulate. You know the mean girl *Cunt* we all hope to know, the mean girl *Cunt* who punches down on less fortunate women, the *Cunt* that co-opts and monetizes everything free and good in life. You know the *Cunt* that flirts with and/or fucks our boyfriends and husbands, the *Cunt* that turns everything into a cunty competition. A woman vs. women competition.

I retreated for a moment into the back of my mind and soul... relaxing... exhaling... breathing.... I thought silently of Appalachia and her winding roads with purple mountains. I thought, *Thank God I'm from West Virginia... Thank God I'm a country girl.*

Mr. Appleton was working past retirement, a balding, fat, divorced man in his late sixties (66-69). He was divorced from reality, divorced from himself — an angry bureaucrat. A bureaucrat wrapped up in the cosmopolitan and corrupt lifestyle in the "Capital Region." The *Capital Region* of the Empire State where Mr. Appleton was a suave janitor with an engineer's degree from Rensselaer Polytechnic Institute (RPI). Abe would hold court wearing his maroon RPI sweatshirt (misprinted RIP) on casual Fridays which matched his late sixties, mommy milk-toast body. There he'd be, in all his glory, flirting and mingling with his mop bucket in our lunchroom.

Mr. Appleton would say, "Don't forget the Empire State's Golden Laws: One (1) for you; six (6) for me. One half (1/2) for you; twelve (12) for me. One quarter (1/4) for you; twenty-four (24) for me."

I would say, "Thank you," pretending to take my dollar seventy-five ($1.75) pay. I look down at my Empire allowance and say in an adoring manner, "You're too generous, Emperor."

People's Exhibit B – Mr. Appleton
with RPI Sweatshirt Misprinted

Mr. Appleton would pretend to think for a moment and then say, "You're right," and snatch back an imaginary dollar from me, taking on an air of Federal importance and arrogance - reclining and enjoying life in his Emperor easy chair.

When not clowning around, Mr. Appleton lived to fly-fish in the North Country of *Upstate* New York. That's where he's proudly from, and the North Country citizens quietly consider the rest of the population of the Empire State south and west of Saratoga Springs as some low-class Appalachian invader to their quiet Adirondack lifestyle. Mr. Appleton's Child Protective Services (CPS) job in Albany (which was his *Downstate* / NYC) was his service, his patriotism, or charity for the Empire State. This charity became a duty when the Appleton name became synonymous with a certain Appalachian video that went internationally viral on the internet in 2010.

The video was of Mr. Appleton's brother, Robert Appleton Jr., an officer of the law and obviously the sexy son, in police uniform, dragging his wife by her hair out of their double-wide trailer. Junior dragged her to his cop car guzzling a beer and then threw her in the back. Abe's brother jumped in his cop car and sped off with the lights a-twirling and the sirens a-swirling. Now for those from Appalachia, that scene there is played out every day, but Big-Ass Appleton Junior, besides being on candid camera, was also on the North Country police clock.

It was an ominous video but proved not a thing, except that New York State police and her citizens live within an insane police-state. Of course, no Empire citizen can speak about this insanity (Wall of Blue) because every citizen in the Empire State had already signed (unbeknownst to *Them*) a Non-Disclosure Agreement (NDA) to never discus the Empire when they signed their New York State taxes.

New Yorkers also seem to have collectively bargained that self-destructive insanity is okay as long as their Gross Domestic Product (GDP) is positive. Although, the accountant signing off on the Empire's GDP account must be approved and certified by Vinny, Vinny, and Vinny's Anti-Corruption Unit (ACU). The citizens of the New York Empire State have also agreed (in abstention) that they won't discuss the possibility of their life being criminal or, God forbid... sinful.

However, when the global internet shone a light on Officer Robert Appleton's Adirondack ass up north, it was not a pretty sight. This Appalachian video was a sign of commitment in the Empire. Everywhere else, it was a revelation of a criminal third-world police force. Because it turned out that Robert Appleton Jr. was the son of the local chief of police, Bob Appleton (Abraham's father). And because Appleton Jr.'s double-wide life / police-officer life included convictions of using / selling crack, domestic abuse, and endangering the welfare of children; and because he had two (2) children with two (2) different women, the Empire haters from around the world eventually moved on to the next police brutality incident, as it is impossible to keep up with the police-state abuse in the Empire. This is no Empire mistake.

That's because a criminal allegation against Empire Governor Cuomo or a State police officer (*Them*) is only fake news, a rumor.... For *Us* unprotected souls in the Empire, a criminal allegation against an Emperor, cop, or bureaucrat is a Special Weapons and Tactics (SWAT) raid. The SWAT raid will be followed up with a New York State Tax Department Audit, an Empire Receiver Appointment, the confiscation and forfeiture of your property, and then an All-Points Bulletin (APB) arrest warrant. For *Us* in the feudal Empire - life is incarceration without bail.

Mr. Appleton walked over to his large windows that overlooked a perpetual gray dinge filled with snow and shadows, and he repeated his introduction to himself looking out the window giggling, "One (1) for you; six (6) for me. One half (1/2) for you; twelve (12) for me. One quarter (1/4) for you; twenty-four (24) for me."

Mr. Appleton's argyle sweater vest (that was rumored to be worn in his graduation photo from RPI in 1986) jiggled as he laughed. It was worn religiously on Monday, Wednesday, and Friday. On Tuesday and Thursday, he wore his special "Blue-period" sweater vest with a dingy white shirt that gave him a fat Catholic nun style with real manly body odor authority. Abe had turquoise framed glasses with lady-like, rosary-bead-looking eyeglass holders that matched the color of his Scottish / English rusty-iron beard and blood.

Mr. Appleton's stunning Chief Executive Officer, Vice President, Assistant Manager (CEOVPAM) view from his Empire Plaza office was thirteen (13) flights above Albany. The office was befitting of a tax man of the Empire, a tax man of the world. It was dismal, ominous, mysterious, out of place, and filled with tremendous, unnecessary stress and gravitas. There were architectural and structural mistakes, and no one could figure *Them* out. Therefore, everything in Albany is awkward.

The expansive view looked south and was of the Hudson Valley. The view was always beautiful in my eyes, and as always, every morning I walked over to Appleton and joined him, waiting and looking for the Emperor's sun to shine in our Hudson Valley.

1
2
3
4
5
6
7
8
9
10
11
12
13
14
15
16
17
18
19
20
21
22
23
24
25
26
27
28
29
30
31
32
33
34
35
36
37
38
39
40
41
42

Chapter 5

HUDSON VALLEY PAINTINGS AND OPERATION:

MOTHER'S DAY MADNESS

1   Mr. Appleton's view almost matched the five (5) or
2   six (6) very cheap Thomas Kinkade posters expen-
3   sively and exquisitely framed on his office walls.
4   The posters were the aesthetic evolution coming
5   from the Hudson Valley School of painters in the
6   mid-1900s. Appleton constantly said he "*Loved* the
7   Valley painters," as if our Cro-Mag Albany work
8   associates were to understand what *Valley* he was
9   talking about. Thomas Kinkade and the Hudson Valley
10 painters painted with visions not of America or
11 New York, but of the European Empire and Romantic
12 idealism. The painters tried to bring a feudal and
13 sentimental painting style to America. Appleton's
14 sunrise posters were greedy, glossy euro-trash with
15 fascist hope, and they all looked identical to me.
16 The paintings were aesthetically the opposite color
17 scheme of reality. The posters were polite and
18 grandiose landscapes when Appalachia certainly is
19 not polite. Appalachia is as intimate as a hushed
20 and vacant church and was as mean as water mocca-
21 sins and blood-sucking leeches. And of course: we
22 are as slothful as sin.
23
24

These Sunday-painters never let the accurate
Iroquois sunshine or the truthful Onondaga clouds
silently slide by during a cold September moon.
Painters Thomas Cole, Frederic Church, and Albert
Bierstadt were Hudson Valley painters working for
the Emperor's daughter's hand in marriage. Loyalist-
royalist painters even back then in 1850 created
false gods and false images of God. They painted
the Emperor's image or view – of the *Real* for royalist-loyalists – for *Them*. The Hudson Valley school
never painted or expressed a human's view, a painter's view, or even an artist's view – for *Us*. These
fainthearted souls couldn't handle the *Other* or the
Real... which is what the true painter paints.

I critique and connect these fine art dots here and
now, Family Court and Good Reader, with the painter
Thomas Kinkade – "The painter of light." The Hudson
Valley painters were the foundation for Kinkade
to build his delusionary customer base. Kinkade
is a Christian poster-printer and not a painter.
He franchised almost three hundred and fifty (350)
galleries and had these gallery franchises sell
his posters as "Paintings" to gullible Christians
at after-church basement sales. You could also
order one of his "Paintings" through the mail as a
Christian opportunity or indulgence.

Kinkade mostly had his assistants print lame fairy-
tales with mountains, rivers, and cottages. The
paintings are aesthetically a cliché, but they sell
big-time. His printing company in 2004 said: One (1)
in twenty (20) American homes had a Kinkade poster.
Even after Kinkade overdosed (OD) on alcohol and
Valium in 2012, his company still generates over
one hundred and ten million ($110,000,000) dollars
per year. But in the high-end NYC *avant-garde* fine
art world – Kinkade was and is a joke. I'll leave
you, Family Court, Good Reader, and maybe a "Good
Looker," with the wise words of Joan Didion and
will rest my fine art case on her sharp critique:

> *A Kinkade painting was typically rendered in*
> *slightly surreal pastels. It typically fea-*
> *tured a cottage or a house of such insistent*
> *coziness as to seem actually sinister, sug-*
> *gestive of a trap designed to attract Hansel*
> *and Gretel. Every window was lit, to lurid*
> *effect, as if the interior of the structure*
> *might be on fire. I call this the Kincade*
> *glow.*

Mr. Appleton's glowing, glaring, and molten poster propaganda was mall art in between water-bongs, black-light posters, and back rooms for fake identification (ID). These paintings are paint-by-numbers for despots and degenerates. Of course, the sunny Kinkade prints (of the *Real*) fought with Appleton's *Real* view of the *Other:* The view out the window from within the Empire of the gray, sooty society, the scorched earth of *Upstate* that every State in America has. The mind-numbing violence of Appalachian silence will drive you up a wall, but the cicada and bullfrog peepers keep the time. It's silent, patient, and fast at the same time in *Upstate* Appalachia, and that is the friction of *Nothing.*

Nowhere is this Appalachian friction better realized than in George Bingham's painting titled "Fur Traders Descending the Missouri," 1845. As opposed to the human-less Hudson Valley paintings, this American painting is focused on the troubled souls of humans and animals in transit. The painting is composed of a man, a boy, and a fox, floating only inches above the Missouri River in a skiff. The man and boy are eloquently dressed in Huck Finn majesty with flouncy blouses and leg-of-mutton sleeves. The man is rowing the skiff and beaming below a red-striped cap. The boy is in the middle of the boat, and he is rocking Native American pants with gold trim. The man is smoking a corncob pipe and looks dodgy and dangerous. The boy is leaning on their fur cargo and resting his head in his hand. The boy is apprehensively smiling in a sad and grievous manner. He has already seen too much, as his dark black eyes testify.

The black fox, which looks like a large cat, is tethered to the bow of the boat and acts as a female figurehead calming the stormy seas ahead. The black fox is marvelously painted again within the reflecting Missouri River. Sitting in another dimension in the sunniest and most hopeful part of the painting. The humans are not afforded this respect from George Bingham the painter, as he cuts off the fur-traders reflections and also tell *Us* that there is treacherous water all around as logs and branches stick out of the Missouri River like the tips of icebergs.

In stark contrast to these alarming and desperate sailors is the beautiful and ethereal Appalachian sky full of clouds above them. The pink and creamy horizon line of an island up-close and farther away – a fainter riverside transposes the tricky navigation of river-running. The translucent rosy clouds are really one cloud and offer an opening / a chance in the sailor's immediate future. But the fur-traders sit on silent and unstable water so still that it reflects their world like a peaceful glass mirror. But, here within that peace is the mind-numbing savagery of Appalachian silence that will drive you up a wall, and as I wrote – the cicada and bullfrog peepers keep the time. The fur-trader painting is silent, patient, and fast at the same time, and that is the song of Appalachia.

Operation: *Mother's Day Madness*

Mr. Appleton questioned me, "I hear you're off to Allegheny this weekend?" looking out the window with eyes peeled and darting about, looking for something in the woods or on the horizon line.

I agreed with my eyes and face and then replied, "Two (2) for one (1) on Mother's Day," while looking out at the foggy morning thirteen (13) floors up. The clouds were hiding in the nook and crannies of Hudson Valley, stuck to the cold earth like State Fair cotton candy. The white hook and pile clouds were thick cream cheese floating / expanding into constant new white shapes like an ethereal mitosis.

Mr. Appleton's office ceiling was covered with large asbestos tiles. It was a large matrix that matched the subtle gray-and-white granite floors I stood on. The granite floors, maybe four (4) feet thick, were sectioned symmetrically with thin stainless-steel beads at identical intervals. The air smelled clean and steely; it tasted like the atmosphere was filtered, monitored, and slightly electric like static electricity. Mr. Appleton's graphic office was comforting if you enjoyed plotting... or being plotted.

Mr. Appleton choked, gasped, and stuttered, "M-M-Mo-Mo-Moth-Moth-Mother's Daayy" with a look of astonished mama's-boy horror - with a look of shock and awe....

He had obviously forgotten it was the Friday before the second Sunday in May - Mother's Day. A national holiday; far from my West Virginia heart of *Motherhood,* far from my mother's heart in Appalachia, America. Mr. Appleton started listing in his mind the gifts and cards he needed to get immediately for the many mothers in his life.

Mr. Appleton whispered to himself, "Some I can mail, some I need to drop off in mailboxes discreetly, and some will have to be delivered with flowers majestically." He looked scared, as if he feared for his life.

In Mr. Appleton's office, the heating, venting, and air conditioning (HVAC) was set at sixty-five (65) degrees with clean air filters the size of small houses and no humidity, which produced a perfect metallic air. This is the hum of the Empire: a vibrating and industrial vibrato similar to a fan, greased and churning at two hundred (200) revolutions per minute (RPM).

This empirical square wave is frustratingly brutish, yet polite and "Good" like a drugged child: calm, clean, organized, and soulless. Mr. Appleton, the man-child in his office, looked and acted like an Amish monkey in a sound-lab experiment.

It seemed as if one of the sound-lab scientists had a sense of humor and wanted to test his hypothesis of whether Empire State eunuchs could reproduce even after they had evolved into being asexual. Like most Empire men who are cheap bastards, Mr. Appleton was emasculated and divorced from his masculinity because his ex-wife and her divorce lawyers had taken turns biting it off for him.

I hung around in *Upstate* silence in Mr. Appleton's office and then excused myself. There was Mr. Appleton, waving me goodbye, saying, "Good luck, I think Allegheny is somewhere near California," even though Mr. Appleton knew the tax map's section, map, and lot numbers of every property within the Empire State.

From a tiny property lot of green and brown scrub brush on the very end of Long Island in Montauk. There it sits on a Camp Hero ledge that smells of seaweed, time travel, and overlooks the majestic Atlantic Ocean. The incessant waves roll around beautiful rocks in the ebb and flow of the shore break. These rocks and the tumbling noises they make are from another world and transcendental. Lot #07286 0300 076000.

To a small property lot of deciduous trees on a tiny island in the middle of the Finger Lakes. The glistening, loud, blue-gray river runs south around the island as salmon swim north. The glassy water flows from Niagara Falls, and it smells like a damp, clean, and shaded house. The tree canopy is high because of the tall hemlocks, but the floor and air are the color of rusty red needles from the white pines. The red floor glows as the sap races around the trees on this majestic island. Even there, Mr. Appleton knew the Empire's section, map, and lot number. Lot #00910 058 028720.

There among the pines on an island with salmon flying through the air in one direction and a large river of water flowing in the opposite, there, Mr. Appleton knew everything but *loved* and/or respected not a thing. Appleton's lack of gratitude was his church, mosque, and/or synagogue. For this "Abrahamic Brother" and/or *Abe-Bro* was a religionist numbering what could not be numbered. This was Abe Appleton's empirical garden of agony.

I half saluted Mr. Appleton hard and sharp, and then held my salute, wishing him a "Happy Mother's Day."

Mr. Appleton straightened up, came to attention, and said, "Sorry, Officer Munda, I've got some issues..." He saluted me like a tired Commanding Officer (CO) drowning within and caught up in the bureaucracy of being a CO. He then said, "Do what you are here to do, Munda, and walk like you have a purpose!"

I finished my sharp salute and looked Appleton in the eye and silently nodded my head in silence as we both glided away from each other on those wise words, "Do what you are here to do, and walk like you have a purpose!"

I deeply like Mr. Appleton for his grandpa United

States Marine advice he always gives me. The Marines' *"Semper Fi"* motto in Latin means "Always Faithful," which is damn close to *Constant Perseverance....* I said out loud in a dark, bureaucratic, concrete Albany building, and in a human-less hallway, on a meaningless morning, to no one in particular: "Walk like *Constant Perseverance....*"

Wise words in the Albany *Capital Region* are a rarity... just as "Wise Albany" and/or "Good Albany" are words rarely heard in the Empire. Insert any American Capital city, from any State, and that same empirical oxymoron will be produced: Wise Harrisburg, Pennsylvania? Wise Little Rock, Arkansas? Wise Austin, Texas? Wise Tallahassee, Florida? Wise Sacramento, California? Wise Richmond, Virginia? Wise Olympia, Washington?

And if you really want to understand my hypothesis, then insert the Capital of the United States. Wise Washington, DC? You get my point, Good Reader? Easy money makes people stupid, as these metaphysical financial rivers flow both ways. Just as the Hudson River actually flows both ways... to and fro beside Manhattan – the Empire that never sleeps.

Albany's third-world budget produces an Empire and/ or "Civilization" by living thirty (30) years ahead of time within municipal debt financed by Wall Street loan sharks. No one sleeps when the Capitol spits out capital. Legislative capital, Special Committee capital, Department of Education capital, Police Department capital, State Emergency capital, Department of Transportation capital. Very extra, special, top-secret pork-barreling committee capital. You-name-it capital pours out of the Capitol. This is child abuse or, in my Grandma Anna's language, "We are robbing Peter to pay Paul." In the Empire, we rob our children to pay the Empire, we cheat and deprive our children to pay Vinny the loan shark on Wall Street.

Three (3) Vinnies in a Room then play spin-the bottle. Vinny Cuomo spins the bottle, and it rattles
and bobbles as the mouth spins and whistles like a
mourning dove in flight. It hoots within a slowing white flutter; the flight is over, the bottle
slows, the bottle stops. Vinny Cuomo French kisses
Vinny Silver in a vulgar and misogynist way; Vinny
Skelos gets jealous.... Vinny Cuomo spins the bottle again.   Again, round and round, where does
it go? Nobody knows. Round and round, the bottle
slows, round and round, nobody knows....

The foreplay is over, and now the emperors-in-
training battle with shivs, razors, and sharpened
toothbrushes like prison inmates in Attica. Albany
is the the good-cop, while *downstate*, his buddy
the bad-cop, was busy fleecing the world for the
last twenty-five (25) years. All protected by the
"Wall of Blue." The *Downstate* taxes from Madison
Avenue, Fashion Avenue, Silicon Avenue, and Wall
Street allowed New York Appalachia the cushiest
Upstate redneck life that borrowed money can buy.
This is the same empirical "Democratic" scam that
Boss Tweed from Tammany Hall planted and that New
York Democrats have cultivated and improved upon
since 1850.

Albany, architecturally and socially, is more like
a third-world Communist town than a capitalist
Capital town. Albany the gray gulag is more Roman
in turns of bribery and extortion. Albany is Cyprus
on the Hudson. Albany allows the Empire State's
political goons to fight and grovel for their blood
money as comrades, crooks, and oligarchs live happily within its control-fraud laws. These oligarchs
in underpants are wired up in *Upstate* silence as
the *Downstate* mafia slice and dice trillions of
dollars for the emperors and empresses first. And
then if there is any money left over within their
trickle-down American economics, they distribute
the Empire's wealth as it's always been dispersed
throughout time by the Empire and the royal King's

accountant. For it's just as Mr. Appleton explains: "One (1) for you; six (6) for me. One half (1/2) for you; twelve (12) for me. One quarter (1/4) for you; twenty-four (24) for me."

Chapter 6

COMPLAINING ABOUT COMPLAINING

I'm driving way too fast on Route 86 headed west out of Binghamton, and it's about 1:30 a.m. I'm about two and a half (2 1/2) hours from my first surveillance position, and I'm starting to get sleepy. I hate this part of driving at night... when you doze off driving seventy-two miles per hour (72 mph) and then wake up in a frantic split second, spazzing out because you thought you'd been really sleeping for hours. That dozing-while-driving starts trickling into my Appalachian Spring drive as I hit a large piece of "Black-Ice" on a bridge.

I should have known better... but, dear Family Court and Good Reader, and for those of you who don't live with *Black-Ice*, let me explain this glassy black devil in metaphysical terms.

The sensation of driving on *Black-Ice* is similar to dreaming... but the dream is for tomato-slicer cars also. We are just the dozing victim, the mushy tomato dozing inside the car, inside a two (2) ton tomato-slicer car going seventy-two miles per hour (72mph) down the road — dozing.

The tomato-slicer car in the cold parts of America

looks for its friend – Mr. Black Ice. The superhost
– Mr. Black Ice – hides on the dark and shady side
of the road; Mr. Black Ice hides on bridges and
low-lying roads. "Mr. B," as he sometimes goes by,
will make you dream tomato-slicer dreams, but you
ask: why would a mushy, dozing tomato like myself
dream tomato-slicer dreams?

That's because your life flashes in front of you
when you hit the *Black-Ice*. Your mushy life is
instantaneously out of control in a two (2) ton
tomato-slicer at seventy-two miles per hour (72
mph). And only a millisecond ago, your little life
was firmly in control, but now your little life
is out of your control. And in your mind, you see
your life's essence. Your little life becomes a
very little flash that is terrifying in its insig-
nificance. You want this self-realizing horror to
stop as your heart flutters, skips a beat, and then
starts palpitating. Your throat goes dry, and you
cannot swallow anymore. You apply the brakes – but
the car brakes don't work anymore. Mushy tomato
pushes the gas – but the gas doesn't work anymore.
Mushy in the car turns the steering wheel left, but
the tomato-slicer car turns right. Mushy in the
car turns the steering wheel right, but the tomato-slicer car turns left. Your little drive down
the highway turns into a life-changing catastrophic
winter tragedy amongst many *Black-Ice* Appalachian
tragedies.

On *Black-Ice* you become a passenger within your life
and inside your car instead of being the driver.
As the tomato-slicer car silently slides uncon-
trollably towards the left and bumps off the median
divider, your tomato-slicer car is now spinning
right slowly and quietly, completing a full three-
hundred-and-sixty (360) degree revolution. This
dreamy point of view (POV) while spinning on *Black-
Ice* can be a life-changing and scarring event. But
it doesn't have to be, because the antidote for
Black-Ice is to be good with the dream world, to be

good with the right-side of your brain. And most important, to be good with the Free-Grace of God.

No one wants to imagine their mushy body being put through a tomato slicer, but when your car: a two (2) ton piece of metal and glass, flips and rolls-over ten (10) times before hitting a tree - you too will look like a sliced-up tomato. And everyone that lives in frigid America shares this winter nightmare about *Black-Ice*. But the saddening life-flash, the sliced-up tomato dream actually helps *Us* northern Appalachians every winter to be shocked out of our stupor of driving too fast during the winter. This nightmarish winter vision in front of you suddenly declares, "You're a mushy tomato - you should not be driving around in a tomato-slicer car! Take a walk, fatty - you cannot handle fast!"

But there one sits, even after this wintry revela-tion, still going seventy-two miles per hour (72 mph) after just completing a three-sixty (360) on *Black-Ice* over the frozen bridge and then right-ing oneself's car by some grace of God. There one coasts along, shaking in *Black-Ice* anxiety with sweaty palms, white knuckles, a ghostly complexion, a lame excuse, and a lot more gray hairs. This is *Black-Ice* Appalachia.

Realizing I cannot handle fast right now, I decide to stop for some hot coffee and soak up some of that northern Appalachian nighttime ambiance. I pull into a gas station near the bottom of the Finger Lakes in a town called Harmony. It's next to Friendship, so I know there are good Quaker founding fathers around. This spot is where Canada and Appalachia join hands and reach all the way down to Alabama and the Gulf of Mexico. This well-worn American path is *the* scorched earth alley. An unnerving alley that gets spiritually claustropho-bic as the horizon lines enlarge. This is the path to the Great Hill and a Western Door to America.

This burnt-over earth of America is the good ground where all of her Great Awakenings first sprouted.

The gas station is barren and flickers with a shaded fluorescent light that hums like a bug-zapper during the long nights of humid summers. On the gas pump there is a notebook page crudely duct-taped to the pump that reads: "No Gas."

The snow flurries gather for a momentary party in the single bluish fluorescent light above the service station. Then the white flakes scurry away into the dark and speckled white night as if the snow forgot they had something to do. The downy snowflakes seem like wild stars within this dark galaxy of Harmony, America. The whiteout of flakes are large and light; they float earthward slowly like paratroopers with large white parachutes enjoying the ride. Or perhaps the plump snowflakes look like dumb moths stuck at a service station light thinking it's Jupiter in the dead heat of an August night.

This station seems to be the last gas station before Lady Chautauqua — before I meet the Lady of the Lake. These service stations in this part of the Empire are not the new national food stores and/or malls with gas pumps. No, this Finger Lake station looks like a 1970s chop-shop garage that deals drugs on the side. As it is in all third-world towns, this station is probably owned by the oldest and slimiest family in town. Every town within poverty has *Them*: the King bully family connected to the crooked banker family or the dubious real estate baron, and their families control not just Main Street, but the Kiwanis Club, the Knights of Columbus, the American Legion, and of course the Big-Daddy Town Fathers on the town council. Like in all third-world towns, these Appalachian people will kill you for a penny or their pride.

I open the store door, and a few cowbells jingle and

jangle. The bells are crudely attached to the wood-
en-and-glass door, yet they harmonize quite nicely.
The bells jingle deceptively on multiple acoustic
levels with light energy and dark, sad paranoia.
This harmony triggers me — I'm back in a third-world
country; I feel at home here in Sandinista, Kabul,
and/or Appalachia. These good-ole-boy or good-ole-
party (GOP) towns and villages in the third-world
maintain a constant state of slow-motion war — a
constant state of poverty. These corrupt little
Appalachian feudal systems with the common folk and
without Wall Street profits make me feel like I'm
on the banana-republic front lines again — still in
the "Theater" of the *Real*.

Coastal America is insulated in its blue-state
blood-money luxury. They don't understand war profiteering and third-world *Nothings* like Managua,
Syria, and Appalachia.

As I walk to the counter, I see a "Gas Station Man"
looking at an old black-and-white television around
eight (8) to ten (10) inches wide. He's in his mid-
fifties (54-56), like me. He's smoking a cigarette;
he doesn't look up, and he's wearing a dirty 1970s
Op-Art bathrobe along with a fine thrift-store boa.
The glamorous 1950s fluffy black boa is made of
black peacock feathers speckled with iridescent
feather eyes shimmering green, gold, and silver.

I walk over to check out the coffee that smells like
rubber or petroleum burning. I fill up in order to
assimilate; I drink in order to taste *Intel*. The
coffee has a bitter, microwaved, burnt taste. I hold
not a cardboard coffee cup, but hot Styrofoam from
the 1960s that seems to be melting with the hot coffee and my hand wrapped around it. My fingers indent
themselves into my plastic petroleum coffee. I take
a quick sip of coffee before the hot plastic balloon
explodes in my hand. I put the coffee down on the
counter, and the *Gas Station Man* looks away from his
black-and-white television. I refocus and realize

People's Exhibit C – Gas Station Man

the *Gas Station Man* is watching horse racing on
the Off-Track Betting (OTB) channel. He looks at
the coffee on the counter and does not look at me.
He takes a drag on his cigarette, blows it in my
direction, and then growls, "Dolla Ninety-nine"
($1.99) as he turns back to the OTB TV.

I put down two (2) bucks and say, "Keep the change."

Gas Station Man is shy at first, looking down as
all Appalachians do when they meet a stranger.
He smiles to himself, as I can see his cheeks
rise. He brays up with his head moving forwards
and backwards like an excited horse. After catch-
ing his Appalachian balance, he says with an ironic
Southern drawl, "Biiigg speeendaa... huuunnnhhh?"

I reply, "Put it on your favorite horse, good man."

Gas Station Man puffs up all aglow and says, "That
favorite bet would on my lucky Lady of the Lake, my
Lady Chautauqua right there." He points to a top-
less Dolly-Parton-type pinup girl on the cover of
one his many antique "Hustler" magazines available
for purchase.

At this same time, a Maine Coon cat sitting high on
a catwalk shelf yawns and cries at the same time.
The cat is looking down at me with a disapproving
scowl. I realize this is a very large black and
white cat as it rises up and stretches its front
legs – never unlocking its eyes from mine. Its
head must be at least two (2) feet high, and it
could weigh around thirty to forty pounds (30-40
lbs). For some reason, female cats don't like me,
and this pussy mama is no different. She starts to
pace back and forth, and then she circles around,
sits down, and settles into herself confidently.
The Maine Coon cat's black-and-white lynx-like ears
twitch, cup, and slide over to me. They face me –
one black and one white - tracking me like a radar
dish - listening to my unsaid mammal language.

Gas Station Man notices I look concerned about the mountain cat stalking me above, but he continues without mentioning his catamount friend perched on the cornice. He says, "Put 'er all on the Lady of the Lake, Big Spenda! Chautauqua Lady is the winner that will set *Us* free!" Then he laughs. His cackling laugh is forced and annoying; it rattles and rolls around like loose nails in a metal coffee can.

The Maine Coon cat tires of watching her owner flirt with another female – so she yawns in my face again, telling me what a boring slut I am. This *lovely* lynx is stunning but dangerous, and she is going out into the night on a mission / on a hunt. She pops up into full stride – her gait is that of a happy-go-lucky fox trotting home after a successful hunt, a bobcat bouncing, or a worriless wolf walking on air. The mama cat, the eternal tigress, prances her way along the high catwalk above me. She walks with *Constant Perseverance*.... She quickly disappears through a broken pane of glass in a transom. I think... "I wish I could go with her."

Gas Station Man asks me, "Headed out to the Seneca's Great Hill casino? Do you have the luck of the Lady?"

I reply, "I hope so; it's Mother's Day!"

Gas Station Man suddenly turns pale white and looks nauseous and scared. He steps backwards as his eyes fog over into a deep, petrified terror. He partially extinguishes his cigarette in his beer while most of the smoldering tobacco melts into the Formica countertop. *Gas Station Man* leans towards me with a look of devastation and stutters in a hushed tone, "Goo-goo-good God, fair lady.... Did you say it is Mo-Mo-Moth-Moth-Mother's Day?"

I say, "It's May 9ᵗʰ / springtime, buddy; make some new coffee!"

He runs his dirty hands through his greasy hair and

seems lost in the deep stress and anxiety males have from possibly forgetting their mothers on Mother's Day.

I break the spell and say, "You got plenty of time, child — pull something together. Mother will forgive you."

But deep in my mind, I know women NEVER forgive anyone or anything! They're like God, our Maker, our Creator: they're mean, vindictive, and especially these days in 2021 – women laugh at each other's pain. We are screeching bullies, we are squawking cowards, it's all very sad for me.... All I can think of is Edith Wharton's concluding words in her masterpiece "Ethan Frome," 1911:

> *And the way they are now, I don't see much*
> *difference between the Frommes up at the farm*
> *and the Frommes down in the graveyard; cept*
> *that down there they're all quiet, and the*
> *women have got to hold their tongues.*

Gas Station Man looks relieved and tells me, "Thank you, Empire lady, thank you!"

He pauses a moment and then continues, "Listen, those Seneca will steal your money and your soul, goddam probably scalp ya. So, you take these carnation flowers for Mother's Day safety."

He reaches over to some fake green and white carnations stuck on an old St. Patrick's Day party cake decoration. The cake hangs next to some porno magazines and below the male enhancer vitamins. He wrestles with the white plastic carnation flowers, as they do not want to leave their cake. *Gas Station Man* continues fighting and leaning on the counter, which is creaking and moving like it might collapse. He mutters something about "That bitch Diana" and then pulls away a white carnation, huffing and puffing. *Gas Station Man* then gingerly places the white carnation in my hand in a polite and professional manner.

Gas Station Man explains, "These were the eyes of a good-natured shepherd... ripped out by the angry Goddess Diana. But now, dear mother, you can change the tides and be a shepherd yourself." He concludes, breathing heavily, "Go, dear mother... and be careful – the Lady of the Lake at Lake Chautauqua will be out... her winds are blowing hard, cold, and bizarre tonight... like every night."

I walk out of the gas station as the jingle bells jangle and jingle. The snow flurries have turned into a sugar-snow and free-fall like lonely cello notes tuning itself for a nocturn. A late-in-the-season white, wet snow with snowflakes the size of silver half dollars. And this blanket of snow sticks to the cold, black, and frozen earth... slowly... like laying white gauze on a bloody wound. I am going to have to slow down now. Things are starting to get strange and slippery. I am entering the Southern Tier, and I am not sure whether I will get through the Western Door to America. And more importantly – will I make it back to the Capitol?

I drive west into the darkness, thinking about Allegheny. It is another rust-belt town, a has-been Town, an *Upstate* / downstate or sidestate from the Capitol city town. Not a college town, a loser town, an old-factory town. Too far north? Too far south? Too far from the turnpike? Too far from the box stores? Not too cool, not fashionable — an American Legion town. A town that every year loses money and everything else that isn't jailed or nailed down – a negative amortized town, a Neg-Am Jam /a NAJ Town. A charity town... unable to pay its snow-plowing costs, much less its educational costs. A NAJ town kept alive by the Empire as a lab experiment for the Mmnicipal debt money-changers to bury as "A positive loss" or "Creative Destruction." A welfare-queen town that kills its children with bad-faith debt. This redneck control fraud allows all of *Us* fat-cow rednecks in *Upstate* to walk around our abandoned Main Streets high in our vacant happiness: milking the Empire, worming the Capitol of capital – but pretending not to be a debtor underwater. This municipal debt makes our children jobless, homeless, and suicidal. This is child abuse.

Markazi, Managua, Allegheny, and all towns *Upstate*, downstate, or side-state from the Capitol of the Empire trickle along within poverty. *Upstate*, zombie traffic, communists within capitalism that call themselves capitalists complain about cracked sidewalks and their "Community." Appalachia in 2021, where thick moribund newspapers sell out quickly and smudge like coal dust on our fingertips. They print what everyone already knows nationally and sell it as homegrown or "Local." Per Psych-Ops *Intelligence* that comes with the Capitol's capital, it's not "Think Globally – Act Locally," but "Worship Globally – Get Fired Locally."

Back at the *Gas Station Man's* service center, the local newspaper is not a paper for *Us*; it is a paper for *Them,* or the *Real*. The Main Street newspapers scattered from the Maine coast down to the Mississippi delta (all compromised by the *Intelligence* community) are not American newspapers, but the Empire's dirty rags. This press, this media, is not for *Us*, but for the *Real* matrix. The functional junky in America religiously reads the penny-saver advertisements, the garage-sale ads, the police reports, and the obituaries. Within the third-world media and its Appalachian colonies around the world, we are only a debt in the expense account, a tool for depreciation, a small ad or obituary in the Empire's paper. Birthing, selling, and dying within the mainstream media (MSM) of *Nothing* and the *Other*.

Allegheny, a gray, greasy, and grumpy town in which

the 8:00 a.m. commute to work / poverty in the year 1821, 1921, or in 2021 is pretty much the same socially and economically as it ever was.

On their dreary commutes to work and school, the mothers and children in Markazi, Managua, or Allegheny all look the same to me. They don't ask questions – they don't check and balance their local government. They are drug addicts and loy- alists that don't misbehave; there is no mischief with these royalist-loyalists who only follow the dealer / the money.

But these royalist-loyalists do complain about com- plaining. The royalty of the Empire complains about the new neighbor that moved in down the street to the building inspector (a professional complainer). Or perhaps the old tribal Elder has a problem, or maybe the good ole Separatist complains about the new laws that don't complain enough. Complaining about this to the tribal chief at the police depart- ment (professional complainers with guns) because this Separatist complainer believes the police are not following the law (a lot of complaints) and therefore is not complaining and/or protecting and serving the citizens enough. The headline and sub- text on the front page of the Markazi, Managua, or Allegheny newspaper, all called "The *Real*," is the same and reads, "The *Real* Is Going Out of Business! Consume and Complain About the *Other*!"

Chamber of commerce and police departments receive "Emergency Funds" from Albany to "Stabilize Main Street Downturn!" This bad-faith debt is the nar- cissist NAJ life; this is the Empire life. Analogous to this entrapment is the mother life of a mother "Gifting" *love* or debt at a time of need, not out of compassion, but out of an opportunity to gain emotional power. Gift-*love* comes with a bill col- lector attached - gifting *love* instead of giving *love* - not in *love* but for *love*'s sake.

The mothers and children in Markazi, Managua, or Allegheny look the same to me when they wave good-bye to each other. Boy-toys and girl-toys that went with suitcases of cash in Markazi and Managua have the same nervous and scared look in their eyes as the interns in Appalachian bus and train stations before they leave for New York City (NYC).

Baby-Boomer parents tell their children – *Them* – that their nonpaying internship is "All for the best." These childlike and trusting eyes say, "We know this cannot be wrong if my mother says, 'It's the right thing to do' and that 'It's all for the best' — can it?" The child in the Empire is lost and abused.

In contrast, the boy-toy intern's mother is always crying out diligently, for perhaps herself... as she hands the child over to the trade and says, "I *love* you." Mother kisses the child; she pushes *Them* away. She kills the child's soul not just with lies; the mother also kills the child's body with emotional abuse, sexual abuse, and physical abuse. The third-world sorrowful mother / *the mater dolorosa* in Allegheny and Markazi are *Red-Queen* sisters with no mercy.

These sisters and their brothers who parrot *Them* complain about complaining at 6:00 p.m. on the early-evening commute from work (poverty / a non-livable wage) in the year 1821, 1921, or in 2021. It has been pretty much the same socially and eco-nomically for brothers and sisters in Appalachia for the last two hundred (200) years. Amongst the afternoon traffic, the children of the Empire bitch and complain about the Empire, but these addicts / these child-junkies will never do anything about the Empire / the dealer. They will never leave the Empire / the dealer - the junkies only complain about complaining.

In Managua, the nuclear, biological, and chemical

(NBC) silent warfare we served to the mothers and
children in their air, water, and food turned *Them*
into emotionally and physically handicapped hos-
tages. The *Intelligence* key is that mother and
child need to *love* their incarcerator (their men)
first before the tribes' children can be turned
into zombie formalists for the Empire. The duopoly
education that the Empire gives to the child in
elementary school is identical to the duopoly election scam or the faux multiple-choice life it gives
the citizen in a control-fraud society.

In these fascist third-world towns, the child /
mother and "The Family" relationship is divided
and conquered first. Whether it be the Kurdistan
Democratic Party (KDP) children in Markazi feeling
like heroes as they call in the United States Air
Force (USAF) airstrikes on their Shia neighbors.
Or perhaps "Family time" within the Sandinista
National Liberation Front (FSLN) is Dad and son
on late-night death squad missions that strengthen
this Central American father-son bond. Or maybe in
Upstate America, the fat Republican white dad in
his Ford (F) F-150 with his obese son called Junior
drive around fence-watching as they listen to angry
AM (*ante meridiem*) talk radio. They are both part
of the Good Ole Party (GOP), and his frat-boy child
is a rising star on the right-wing podcast cir-
cuit. And of course, there in *Upstate* America or
Markazi, the child: the black sheep, the Senator's
son, and/or the dickhead with a no-show job at
the "Consulting" firm is always impregnating and/
or sexually abusing the secretary, who is always –
like *Us* - trying to escape poverty.

I ask my mother, my father, or perhaps my brother
or sister operating the Remote Aircraft Pilot (RAP)
circling above *Us* all right now with their Predator
drone: Why are you *Them*? I ask this cockroach looking at *Us* via a satellite reading these same words
you are reading at this very moment, dear Reader
and Honorable Family Court....

Our letters, numbers, and spaces – nothing is private anymore, nothing is intimate anymore – even reading a good book alone is not yours and yours alone.

The cockroach is never asleep. And these written words are not yours alone. The cockroach calls in your latitude and longitude coordinates and awaits the OK from their commanding officer (CO) for the order to kill-it. The cockroach alien looks at *Us* from his satellite in another dimensional space. The cockroach gazes longingly and emphatically at *Us* – the mother, the father, the brother and sister child – for a few moments. The Empire cockroach looks closer at their pixelated black-and-white Predator screen, looking at me reading this deposition novel. The cockroach looks at both the *Real* and the *Other* at the same time. The cockroach starts to tear up. A teardrop falls from the roach's dead gaze... just as the Predator screen explodes into a fireball. The cockroach doesn't blink as the dust clears. And now I – a book reader – have been replaced with a crater and not just a bug-splat, but a human-splat. The Empire's danger-close life is getting droned while you're killing it, fucking it, and/or perhaps, Good Reader... just reading it.

Allegheny, like all godless *Upstate* third-world towns are void of life – filled up with just too many ghosts that haunt liberty. A Seneca ghost town? A Sunni ghost town? A Sandinista ghost town? Most definitely a Six Nation ghost town for nevermore. Even though the high school football team is called the Mohawks and their white cheerleaders wear short skirts, dancing, chanting, and singing "The Mohawk Rumble." It goes something like:

Going to the Mohawk Rruuumbbllee....

B Aggressive! B E Aggressive!

Hey Cowboy, Hey Soldier!

B Aggressive! B E Aggressive!

Gonna get his scalp? Gonna take the Hill?

B Aggressive! B E Aggressive!

Going to the Mohawk Rruuumbbllee ...

B Aggressive! B E Aggressive!

Hey Cowboy, Hey Soldier!

B Aggressive! B E Aggressive!

Gonna get his scalp? Gonna take the Hill?

B Aggressive! B E Aggressive!

Allegheny, dry on imagination, dry on capital — lives like outdoor rec-time while in prison. It lives like casual Fridays at a shitty job; it lives like pizza night at Attica State Prison. Allegheny lives like Lenten fish-fries served by Catholic priests in church basements that are way too creepy and way too fishy.

Casual and foul prison reminds me of that first letter from my grandmother, Anna Jarvis, whom I mentioned earlier in this Deposition. As I wrote earlier, my grandma started Mother's Day as a day outside the house for women to unite as a political force against war-mongering politicians and the war industry. Granny Jarvis wrote:

My Dearest Constantia,

I hope you receive this note and new book in the great form I had last seen you. It was Mother's Day at the Philadelphia Society Ball, and you shone like an angel!

I must confess I'm finally in love with a

"Mary" and no, not the Catholic-made "Mary"
but Mary Wollstonecraft! I just finished her
enclosed book, "<u>A Vindication of the Rights</u>
<u>of Woman</u>*."*

She, like me, believes in a woman's education
and raising their voice against our misog-
ynist society. She calls Northeast women
"Spaniels," "Toys," and "Capricious tyrants
living for the pleasure of men in a gilded
prison."

In this book - that made me question my
guilty ways and blush - Wollstonecraft elab-
orates on women's vanity: "They are slaves
to their looks as a Virgin Mother / a Mater
Dolorosa (sorrowful mother) and/or an
Eve-tyrant."

Connie, please pardon my dire outlook, but
looking at the Northeast women here in 1890,
I must agree. Wollstonecraft also has the
vision in her book to propose that "Men need
to help women, but these progressive men
should not become feminized men or sentimen-
tal men, for then women will have no position
in civilization."

Mary Wollstonecraft dug in for too many
pages, in my opinion, writing to the
"Natural" common woman, the masses, and the
forgotten woman. Mary Wollstonecraft believes
the idle rich with their "Royal soldiers,
both male and female, is an unnatural state
of lasciviousness that defeats all happi-
ness." Mary can be too high on her soapbox,
and for God's sake don't tell anyone, but
we're going to meet again this July 4th at
Cape May.

My dearest Connie, I imagine this
Wollstonecraft as Lady Liberty or Marianne in

*that great Romantic and Enlightened paint-
ing by Delacroix titled "<u>Liberty Leading the
People</u>," 1830.   There she is — Marianne or
Liberty in tatters, standing on the dead and
half dead with her children, double-fisted
with revolvers blazing, and she leads them
all. Liberty leads all men. She leads with
that look! That Sophia look, that divine
spark look. She leads the top hat and the
scallywag. Liberty leads humanity for the
"Good ole cause." Liberty leads with heart
exposed and bayonet drawn! God Bless her
heart and her sword!*

*Please keep the vindication book when you're
done, and I hope your spring in West Virginia
has been peaceful and relaxing. Please don't
hesitate to write to me and sing me those
Appalachian songs when time allows.*

Yours Affectionately and Forever,

Grandma Anna Jarvis

I like this letter because when I imagine Lady
Liberty charging — all I can picture is this bad-
ass woman chasing away the Empire's *Three (3) Men
in Roman Circle Jerk*. Liberty is chasing away the
three (3) Vinnies. Liberty runs the bad joke out of
town on a rail. The three feminized and sentimental Vinnies run from the room in Albany with one
hundred and fifty billion ($150,000,000,000) dol-
lars still just sitting there. What is left in the
Empire State after the ambulance-chasing legislatures are run out of town? Does the sky fall? Does
the sun come out tomorrow morning? Will the money
still be there?

Regardless, who cares about the warm sun and endless sky, because right now it's a cold and bitter
morning in Appalachia and I've just arrived at the
Seneca Great Hill casino.

Nighttime is my yang time, it's *Intel* time, it's mother's time, it's Empire *Intelligence* time.

I'm a motherly spy; the *Other* and *Nothing* are my tradecraft and theater. I'm a supporting ghost, a supporting spook, and/or a supporting actress on a dim stage and not on my mark. I stand far away from the lonely X spotlight that marks my spot. As a yang woman, I'm shadowy, I'm cloudy as I fight with my *Sister X* and the *Other*.... I'm balanced yet invisible — my time.

Chapter 7

<u>3:33 A.M. - MOTHER IS ARRESTED BY HER ELDERS, OR, COMPLAINT #21-4532</u>

I walk into the Seneca Nation casino main floor and take a seat at a slot machine. The slot machine is called "Plato's Pay-o-la!" It's dark and masculine like a handsome soldier; it's plastic and friendly like an arcade game. I relax and take a seat in its easy chair, but suddenly it becomes not a dimly lit planetarium but a seizure-inducing delirium. Synthesized trumpets greet me with an escalating scale and then roar "Charge!!!" The lights and screen show Plato with rippling muscles, a hard-on, and buxom babes, and of course those pots of gold at the end of the rainbow. I put in one ($1) dollar and pull the slot machine handle; three (3) Greek Gods spin round fast and hard. One by one, they slow down, clicking into place. The first wheel reveals a bucket of gold and a harem of buxom beauties! The second wheel slows, slowing... and lands — it is a philosopher with a dour look handing me books and pamphlets. The third wheel slows... it lands not on the philosopher, but on the Greek thinker leaning over on his fist and knee. "Plato's Pay-o-la," the progressive slot machine, goes to sleep, shutting all its lights down. It makes a heavy snoring sound

People's Exhibit D — "Plato's Pay-o-la"

like on silly cartoons, implying I had tilted the game and/or lost the game.

"Plato's Pay-o-la," the progressive seducer, suddenly comes alive again. Inebriated again with dark lights and outer-space sounds, it flashes Plato with oiled muscles, shapely babes, and of course those pots of gold. Lights twinkle and sparkle as I think... *should I put another dollar into this machine?*

The smell of dirty ashtrays and perverted basements fills my nose. Instinctually, this makes me antsy. So, I'm up and moving. I smell *Intel*.... Aesthetically, I'm at an amusement park; financially... I'm at a shakedown. I check my strapped Glock to make sure I'm still locked, cocked, and ready to rock. I make sure I have my wallet still tucked into my jacket... tucked far away — out of reach.

Overweight, white Midwesterners mingle with stern-looking Canadians. They look biologically related — the royal white Canadian and the American parent with the very fat and very white American kid who's always misbehaving. Food dribbles out of the adult Americans' mouths and litters their paths on the red-and-orange postmodern wall-to-wall rug that covers the ten-thousand (10,000) square-foot casino. The Canadians whisper to themselves, giggling in snarky ways as the drunk Americans make a mess. These two English colony children squabble here at the amusement park of the British Empire's first and longest-lasting ally in America — the Seneca Native American Indians.

The retired Toronto and Buffalo couples on vacation wander around, spaced-out and blimpy, looking for something to eat or buy. They float or swim slowly, looking like white whales from the same pod and/or school. These Beverly Hill hillbillies don't realize they're in the savages' pot - being boiled alive. They fight like Canucks and Gringos fighting for a scorched-earth salvation as the Turtle

God slowly and methodically takes a step, crushing *Them*. They are being boiled alive in a large and black Seneca Indian crucible that has welded on the side: "Made in London."

Honorable Family Court and Dear Reader, please do not forget that I sell *Intelligence* to the *Other*. I sell *Intel* to *Them*. And if ever asked about my life... I will reply like my hero, Ollie North, by stating proudly, "I do not recall."

I see the target mother in regard to Complaint #21-4532. The mother, Barbara Dalton, has been accused anonymously of child abuse. Barbara Dalton is sixty-two (62) years old and seems to be going on six hundred and thirty-nine (639). She is the mother of three (3) children and grandmother to two (2) children. She is picking up dirty ashtrays at the Seneca Indian Casino where she works roughly forty (40) hours a week. Barb, as she goes by, works the graveyard shift (10:00 p.m. – 6:00 a.m., Wednesday – Monday) for eight dollars and fifty cents ($8.50) an hour, before taxes, and receives a weekly pay-check of roughly two hundred and fifteen dollars ($215.00). Barbara's endurance is pure survival, as her husband is a stay-at-home asshole on a social security disability check ($485) that he does not share with her or his family. Barbara's clothes are her finest Allegheny thrift-store and garage-sale finds ($20) mixed with dollar-store specials of the week ($12). This is third-world poverty in the Empire State of America.

Barbara has a fancy for pastel sweatshirts (light pink and blue) with prints of unicorns and wolves fashioned with sequins or beads woven in to give the sweatshirt an *Upstate* flare. She wears exclu-sively acid-washed blue jeans (even to bed) that she thinks makes her look young and hip. But they really make Barb look homeless and fifteen (15) years older than she is. Barbara's homeless fash-ion and acid-washed life costs Seventh Avenue (7th

Ave.) twenty-two cents ($0.22) a pair from China. The fashion industry *Downstate* seems to have dumped their "Irregulars" of unicorns, wolves, and acid-washed jeans to this back-forty (40) of society. The lampooned of America, the forgotten America, the *Upstate* America, the Redneck-ville, the Bum-Fuck-ville. This Where-ville comes after an Appalachian is asked: "Where are you from? Oh... Where-ville... isn't that over by *Other*-ville? Oh, no... well, never heard of it."

Here in Appalachia, here in *Where-ville*, the infinite supply of unicorns, wolves, and acid-washed jeans is a Barbara uniform. This "Fast Fashion" is mixed with *DOD* Battle Dress Uniforms (BDU) and the "Charity" from church thrift stores, and Salvation Army thrift stores. The resulting fashion again is the "Charity Soldier." Barb's gray, ashen skin has no makeup, and she has a jolly Appalachian disposition founded on Judeo-Christian predestiny and souped up to a methamphetamine-induced manifest destiny.

I watch Barbara as she looks across the mirrored gambling casino hall. The red-and-yellow lights shine brightly overhead, glaring back at the blinking and flashing slot machines that are never turned off. The full spectrum of these colors and lights blinks and reflects in Barbara's thick glasses. The casino hall is an empty monetary whorehouse where Barbara cleans up the sins of the financially stupid and desperate. Barb is about five foot three inches (5'3"), one hundred and ten (110) pounds. She is a svelte and scrawny woman with big bones, sharp elbows, and a hunched back. Barbara's deoxyribonucleic acid (DNA) comes from the Alabama bayous of the South. Underneath her greasy mop of dyed brown and gray hair, she squints at shadows through her thick glasses. At points of crisis, which is about hourly, she closes her left eye in order to focus on things she cares about. Barbara cannot afford to care about much. She travels the world looking at her life with her shaded religious vision.

Barbara appreciates the sterilized cleanup lights and the empty casino that comes on at about 4:30 a.m. when the casino cleanup crew does their thing. Gamblers still mill around, unaware that the hour of the mop is fast approaching. When Barbara starts her shift at 10:00 p.m., she often pretends to clean the customer (white people) restrooms, but really, she is not. Barbara sits on the toilet (feet up off the floor) and reads her King James Bible at the speed of about one (1) page every two (2) days. Barb is not just hiding from the crowds of gamblers that dump their money into this white-devil vacuum run by the Seneca Indians and the Albany Empire. But Barb knows that the white-devil customer bathrooms will be the last place that her boss, Sampa, will find her. The Seneca Indian never go into the whitey's bathrooms... never.

Sampa is a naturally strong and stocky Seneca woman, and she still rules with her British tomahawk given to her by the English redcoats in 1776 to kill crazy American patriots like Barbara. Sampa will never bury her axe and likes to chase Barb around the casino, dreaming of scalping her as she collects a tax-free weekly salary of two thousand three hundred dollars ($2,300 / $113,000 per annum). Barbara Dalton likes to tell other redneck racists that she works at the casino playing "Cowboys and Indians," but really Barbara and the white trash of Allegheny that work at the casino are playing "Indians and Cowboys."

These *Upstate* cowboys take their manly Marlboro breaks in their asbestos-covered "Whitey" break room in the basement next to the boiler rooms where they incessantly discuss the Country Music Network (CMN). "Whitey" is crudely scrawled across the break room front door. There are many other interesting Allegheny comments and drawings in and around their breakroom

and bathroom, even though the Seneca Indians' cleaning / graffiti standards are "A Zero Tolerance" policy. White-cracker's break room and bathroom in the
basement look like a *Downstate* alternative art space
from the 1980s or 1990s, with all the white-trash
diaspora scrawled on the walls. Besides the normal
"Call for a good time" and "KKK" sales pitches, there
is Biblical advice with Proverbs and verse written
up high on the wall and in a commanding font.

The Biblical verse is what all upper executive man-
agement think about when their Wall Street finan-
ciers tell *Them* that they need to downsize labor:

"Come to me, all who labor and are heavy laden, and
I will give you rest." - Matthew 11:28

Underneath this Appalachian mantra, generations of
workers and laborers have signed their names and
sealed their fates not for themselves, but for the
conqueror. On the refrigerator, as if to give all
these Judeo-Christian religious suckers something
to contemplate as they litter the break room with
orange cheezy-puffs and slurp on their colorful
frozen Popsicles, someone has scrawled,

"I will never leave you, nor forsake you." - Joshua
1:5

I'm not sure if Joshua is aware that eighty percent (80%) of these Appalachian workers are obese
and that the cheezy-puff popsicles help ease their
diabetic aches and pains. Maybe Joshua has been
reincarnated as a frozen Popsicle and is truly not
forsaking *Us?*

I say, "Amen," because I *love* sucking and chewing on those Popsicle sticks. Splinters in my red
tongue, splinters in my green tongue, blue tongue,
or splinters in my orange tongue. It doesn't matter because in Appalachia, very little matters. But

colorful tongues in Appalachia is summer fun... all year-round.

This white-cracker dereliction of duty in the base-ment in contrast to the Seneca Indians' break room is astounding. The Seneca's breakroom sits on the seventh (7th) floor penthouse next to the roof deck and the Seneca Grand Council meeting room. It over-looks the Allegheny State Park and Chautauqua Lake.

This proves that white-devil bosses and American Native Indian bosses are the same corrupt prison guards when given the chance to attack, divide, starve, and profit from others. The selfish gene is our only common denominator.

Barbara Dalton doesn't understand where all these gambling people get all their money or why any-one would waste it here gambling at a casino run by the Seneca. The Seneca were their preordained enemy, the American Indian savage, and/or anyone who doesn't believe in Barb's Judeo-Christian God. Barb blames the casino crowds and sold-out shows for REO Speedwagon, or "REO Fag-wagon," as she calls *Them*. And Barb is uncharacteristically accurate with that hypothesis. The white-devil casino bears the resur-recting gift of Barb's employment and/or her police-state poverty ($215 weekly / $10,750 per annum).

I see Barbara slink out of her bathroom Bible study and start to make a break for it across the wide-open plain of the Blackjack, Roulette, and Five (5) Card-Stud sections of the casino floor. I pretend to be interested in a roulette game. Samba materializes out of thin air like a cat on the hunt, like an ace of diamonds from a fixed deck. She trails Barbara hard. Samba is a royal queen of the Iroquois, a goddess of the Turtle Clan. Samba gains on Barbara as a cheetah gains on an antelope in the Serengeti plains of Africa. Barbara feels Samba's hot breath burning a hole in the back of her head, but Barbara is blind as a bat with frequencies and telekinesis.

Barbara starts walking / bouncing off the mingling large, white Midwesterners and Canadians. She's lost in some blind Buckeye limbo dance for floating blimps known as "The *Upstate* Bingo." Samba talks into her wired mic, then stretches out her catlike stride and gait. She picks up the pace and closes in on Barbara. I feel embarrassed as I watch our American femininity devolution play out.

The weak and limping doe with large, honest eyes is always the first to get eaten in every Public Broadcasting Service (PBS) nature special and in every third-world town. Barb is trying to cross the large, open floor in order to get to the basement stairs for phase two (2) of her hiding-out at work, but it doesn't look like she's going make it. Barb is walking forward, looking behind her left and right, with her hands in front of her in order to stop from running into the blimpy gamblers.

Honorable Family Court and Dear Reader, I must confess this is where the toll of being an Empire CPS cop hurts. It's sad to watch people destroy themselves and others. I feel like a sentry in the Dutch Calvary in 1660 on guard duty high on top of Fort Orange overlooking the wild Hudson Valley landscape as the pilgrims skirmish with the local non-friendlies. Just like I did in El Salvador and Kandahar, I watch the burning of the valley as my CO (Commanding Officer) only gets *Us* involved when orders come down from the Empire. We help those *folks* / *tribes* sometimes; we help those other *tribes* / *folks* other times.

The standing-army military is not a humanitarian tool, but a humanitarian wedge. There no rhyme or reason unless you believe our reason is to help / allow these two tribes to kill each other off. It seems we just wait, bringing in more ammunition and more laws so when both of these tribes of *Us* vs. *Them* or was it *Them* vs. *Us*?.... Regardless, when *Us* and *Them* tire of killing each other and/or one side wins, the Empire will just come in and wipe *Them* both out. That's the Judeo-Christian Empire *modus operandi* (MO) for the *Other*.

Barbara is just about to run into the staircase to the basement when her hands suddenly smack into folded arms of a large Seneca man called Red House. Red House is the head of security and has the build of a six-foot-six (6'6") professional wrestler. Red House stands his ground as Barbara blindly feels his folded arms, which look like strong tree branches. Samba follows up from the rear and grabs Barbara by the nape of the neck like a mother cat retrieving her wandering, blind runt of the litter. Red House steps to the side, and Samba drags her bad kitty into the dark "Employees Only" elevator. The arrow points down in red and blinks as the doors close, disembarking into a hell Barbara's Bible has not taught her about.

Life in the Empire... the *Intelligence* life, the counterinsurgency (COIN) life, which turns into the counter-*intelligence* life. This is when *Intelligence* becomes debatable and when justice becomes political. The offensive counter-*intelligence* tribe fights with the defensive counter-*intelligence* tribe — it all becomes standing-army friendly-fire in the report and briefing about the irregular war, the guerilla war, and our American *Intelligent* war.

Food, clothing, and shelter are all Barb can unsuccessfully try to provide for her family. Food, clothing, and shelter trickle down, torturing slowly the tricklee. The trickler is an enemy of mankind, and this is no redcoat / Seneca / Empire trickle-down mistake. These are crimes against humanity by the Empire's turned agents and passive provocateurs. This counter-*intelligence* life has been going on in the New York Empire since the English white-devil came here back in 1664 with their imaginary "Royal" *Intelligence.*

Chapter 8

4:56 A.M. - <u>MOTHER IS DENIED THREE TIMES,</u>
<u>OR, COMPLAINT #21-6154</u>

I've driven approximately two and a half (2 1/2)
miles from the casino, and I'm staked out in my car
on a beautiful public road that has large, gated
driveways but no visible houses. The streetlamps
look like old gas lanterns and flicker with a faux
gas flame. Even though I'm on Highland Avenue, the
rich of Allegheny within their protected luxury are
no match against my *Intel* data-collection tools.
My Dirtbox, Stingray, and Kingfish hear, see, and
record target #6154. My spy-craft tools worm into
the target's Wireless Fidelity (Wi-fi) system, computer network system, and their security camera
system. On one (1) of my three (3) laptops, I can
see, hear, and record ALL of target #6154's activities via her security cameras, computers, televisions, laptops, and all Wi-fi controlled systems,
and software applications (Apps).

Target #6154 is Madeline McHugh, and she has been
anonymously accused of child abuse. Madeline is
sixty-two (62) years old but seems to be going on
thirteen (13). She is the mother of three (3) children and grandmother to two (2) children. Madeline,

Maddy, or Mad is shuffling through one (1) of six (6) designer pocketbooks currently, looking desperately for her Benson and Hedges 100 Gold Premium cigarettes ($17.99 a pack). Madeline is anxious and angry because she cannot find her cigarettes or her "Meds" (Heroin). She believes her youngest daughter, Christa, home for the weekend from her boarding school (approximate cost: ninety-two thousand ($92,000) a year), had stolen her cigarettes and prescribed medicine earlier in the evening. Madeline's cash (approximately six hundred and forty dollars ($640) is also missing, but Mad doesn't care. The situation is escalating because Mad is unable to take her *Meds* to control her exasperating stress, anxiety, and hysteria. Madeline is "Sleeping" in the guest apartment of her twelve-thousand (12,000) square-foot McMansion in Allegheny. It is worth around two million three-hundred thousand dollars ($2,300,000). The guest apartment is on the polar opposite side of the mansion from her bedroom, which she used to share with her husband. The guestroom is where Madeline goes when she cannot sleep, which is where she has been for the last twenty-two (22) years.

Madeline throws her Gucci pocketbook worth about two-thousand, one-hundred dollars ($2,100) across the large plush apartment. Madeline's Chanel Rouge Allure lipstick, which costs one-hundred-and-twenty-five dollars ($125), flies in one direction. The keys to her one-hundred-and-five-thousand-dollar ($105,000) Mercedes station wagon crash onto an eighteen-hundred-dollar ($1,800) fragile glass coffee table. The table seems relieved to shatter and collapse to the floor in a small cloud of shimmering, splintered glass.

Madeline finds an old Hermes wallet worth maybe three thousand dollars ($3,000) that is crudely stuffed with four hundred dollars ($400) cash and a stack of credit cards with over two and a half million dollars ($2,500,000) in available credit. This

People's Exhibit E - A Closet of Pocketbooks
Worth One Million Dollars ($1,000,000)

wallet isn't the wallet Maddy is looking for, so Mad badly throws the Hermes – Son of Zeus – wallet. The wallet sails through the air towards the large windows and is softly enveloped into the apartment's rich auburn and velvety curtains. The wallet that could finance maybe thirty (30) third-world communities for a year is lost in the many creamy folds and waves of the lush imported Italian fabric that costs ninety-five dollars ($95) a yard.

Maddy ignores, or possibly enjoys, the chaos she creates. Mad stomps her way into her twenty (20) foot by thirty (30) foot walk-in closet that most people in Manhattan would call a three-bed apartment (approximately $3,200 a month). Madeline pouts like a bulldog as she relaxes in her walk-in closet with a wet bar, a large-screen television, and a sitting area for guests to watch the dressing-room altar. The altar has three (3) adjustable ceiling-to-floor mirrors and lighting. Madeline sits in the guest sitting area of her dressing room and thinks about how she has no guests to talk to about... about her new outfits, or just talk about anything at all. Maddy's face is in her hands, and she is tearing up – getting very emotional.... Then she suddenly and erratically stands up, paces, and pretends to be happy. Watching Maddy makes me uncomfortable – insanity is sad. It is not something that should be entertained.

Madeline's clothes are the finest couture that an online shopper and a black American Express card can buy from Bum-Fuck, Appalachia. Madeline's hair is dyed Palm-Beach-bimbo-blonde, but it looks more like Fort-Lauderdale-bimbo-yellow. Maddy's hair has been professionally dyed every week for six hundred dollars ($600 total): four hundred and sixty dollars ($460) for cut, wash, and dye – plus a tip of one hundred and forty dollars ($140). Maddy is a grimacing buttered-up blonde Baby Boomer who still dresses and talks like a freshman cheerleader at an expensive school for girls earning their "MRS degree."

Mad is only truly happy and content when dreaming about being happy and content. Maddy prays to the *Real*... but she hides from the *Other* and her *Sister X*. Maddy is the young and spindly sprout after the male gaze has been grafted to her. Madeline is a *Red-Queen* drowning in luxury.

Madeline's Judeo-Christian family dreams didn't exactly play out how she imagined, growing up reading fairy-tales about Cinderella and the Virgin Mary. Madeline lacks control over the world, so she "*Loves*" her family by grunting and grinding *Them* down with "Gift-*love*." Maddy then oinks and snorts for a few more morsels of respect, feed, and/or power with "Need-*love*." Madeline receives no respect from her family and wonders why after mothering, asking, begging, needing, pleading, extorting, bribing, and/or hoarding *Gift-love* (power)... that "*Love*" is not working out for her.

In philosopher C.S. Lewis's review of this self-destructive *Love* behavior, as explained in his novel "*The Four Types of Love*," Madeline fits a "Perverted subhuman" category.

Madeline stumbles into a smaller closet towards the back of the walk-in closet. Madeline looks on shelves through her other pocketbooks, which may contain stale cigarettes. She's looking for her cigarettes because her daughter frequently pilfers them from her. And this larceny is psychologically driving Maddy crazy.

Madeline rifles through her Marc Jacob crocodile pocketbook from a few seasons ago and her Louis Vuitton (Patchwork Collector's Edition) that she used for years, still worth twenty-four thousand six hundred dollars ($24,600) on eBay (EBAY). An older, classy Hermes Birkin bag purchased as a gift, and then a write-off for her husband's business, originally cost one hundred and ten thousand dollars ($110,000), but it is beat up, so it is worth approximately forty-five thousand dollars ($45,000) online. The Hermes bag contains a solitary cigarette butt. Madeline tries to light the squashed cigarette filter with no tobacco left. Madeline lights the filter on fire and inhales deeply. She is finally relaxing while the poison courses through her brain and blood. Maddy slumps to the floor of the closet within a closet within a home. She mutters to herself about her daughter and her headache. She rubs her forehead like an institutionalized teenager.

Mad starts to sob, smoke, and choke alone in the dark closet on this lonely Mother's Day morning. She starts to hyperventilate, blubbering spit and snot out of her mouth and nose. Madeline heaves and convulses, still sucking on the smoking plastic filter cigarette. She smokes it like a desperate pothead smokes a small marijuana roach.

Maddy continues to choke and cry. I feel compelled to run into Madeline's house and administer the Heimlich maneuver, but I restrain myself. Honorable Family Court and Good Reader: my Empire job is to watch and record the demise and the truth of *Motherhood*. I do not get involved – I am a camera.

Madeline continues to choke and smoke like a high-end crack-whore. The smoking filter seems to calm her down a little bit.

I take a break from the luxury-induced discontent. I push eject on my CD player, and out pops out Tim McGraw's "Sundown Heaven Town." I put in an equally scratched CD from my Appalachian life. The album is Shania Twain's "Come on Over." I slowly increase the volume, filling my Ford (F) Interceptor with "Man, I Feel Like a Woman."

I look up from my computer screens and stare outside my Empire *Intel* car. I feel the earth shaking.
The sun sits below the horizon line and is still
out of sight. A gray-blue twilight simmers on the
sun's horizon line as white snow flurries float
down like falling feathers. An Allegheny town snow-
plow and salter slowly drives past me. A grizzled
Appalachian townie with a cigar in his mouth and a
cowboy hat leans out his window. He checks out my
blacked-out cop-car, idling peacefully. The townie
makes numerous mental notes, as the townies are not
just the plows and salt-spreaders of Appalachia,
but the salt and pepper of Appalachia. The townie
job is an Appalachian Union requiring impossible
requirements and pedigree. It is for only the Very
Important People (VIP) of Appalachia, and Lordy...
what a pension!

The salt from the townie's spreader sprays my car
like machine-gun fire. White cotton-candy snowflakes slowly fall and melt on my idling, hot,
black car. The Empire townie nods his head back
at my Empire car as a double agent provocateur for
the Empire *Real*. Townie is an Empire mole, as the
Appalachian good ole boys and their cowboys joined
the Empire a long time ago, believing they were
doing good, believing they had been recruited to
save the patriot, to save the forgotten man / the
common man. But townie was double-crossed by the
Empire, and now they are fighting a losing battle
for food, clothing, and shelter. So, therefore,
townie, who is now in the snowplow, or townie at
the Town Clerk's office, or townie leaning on his
shovel in the summertime in the middle of the highway construction project, is an indentured servant
suffering from "Stockholm Syndrome." In spite of
this, townie cowboy and townie cowgirl are still
the eyes and ears of Empire *Intelligence*.

When you have the Empire politicians, the press,
and the police all on the same page, all on the same
side, all on the same take, the cold-cash *Intel* take

– the opposition to the Empire – is no more. The opposition's opinion is hearsay and blasphemy... and soon to be illegal. And then because you want to check and balance the local Appalachian Empire / the local government, you are now a heretic and a blasphemer – and we all know what happens to *Them*.

I look down at my computer screens again. Madeline thinks really hard about solutions to her nicotine withdrawal. Pills and wine first come to her mind, then lots more pills. Visions of drawers with amber-colored pill bottles and medicine cabinets filled with orangey-brown heroin synthetics and pharmaceuticals give Mad a quick dopamine high. Maddy giggles... surfing her drug-addled high. Her giggling continues in a sinister way....

Shania Twain's chorus comes in perfectly:

"Oh, oh, oh, go totally crazy, forget I'm a lady."

Light-orange and root-beer-colored plastic pharmaceutical bottles filled with pills spill about in Madeline's sassafras luxury. There are pills for the husband, pills for the children, pills for the "Tired" mother, pills for the "Angry" mother, pills for the disobedient daughter, pills for the disobedient doggy, pills for the aggressive and sexy son, and many, many pills to hide the *Real* and mask the *Other*. Mad's pills keep *Nothing* away. But a few days ago, right after her youngest daughter, Christa, came home from school, Maddy's pills disappeared.

Maddy is consumed by the motherly devaluation, the disrespect, and the humiliation of being denied / of being taken advantage of by a thief, by her daughter. Mad prances out of her discombobulated closet-cave within a lady-cave. It is almost 5:40 a.m., and Christa still isn't home after going out with Patrick Pilates last night. Christa is home for Mother's Day dinner, and Madeline thinks how happy she ought to be. But Mad wonders why she isn't happy....

Mad did not realize she was not happy unless she was selling motherhood and believed that to be motherly *love*.

Shania Twain's chorus came back into my Interceptor sound system like a misty fog. "Oh, oh, oh, go totally crazy, forget I'm a lady."

Chapter 9

5:59 A.M. - <u>MOTHER IS CONDEMNED BY HER FAMILY, OR, COMPLAINT #21-4532</u>

I'm trailing Barbara Dalton again as she finishes up her graveyard shift. She is in the back of the vast casino parking lot next to the two (2) or three (3) dumpsters overflowing with trash. Gigantic icebergs or piles of brown, black, and yellow snow stand thirty (30) to forty (40) feet up into the air around *Us*. This is from this past winter's snow. We're boxed in within a dirty igloo within a sky. It smells like garbage outside, so I roll up my windows and switch my car's airflow to internal only (IO). Next to these floating glaciers of snow and downwind from the dumpsters, we all enjoy the silence on Mother's Day morning 2021. Slurpy cup trash blows around this large graph set on a frozen tundra — this is where "Whitey" who works at the casino on the Reservation (REZ) parks.

Barbara seems excited, huddled over and smoking a cigarette with her girlfriend. She and her friend are dancing the Appalachian Winter Two-Step: hopping from one foot to the other in order to keep warm and not become frozen to the ground. They seem to be appreciating the dawn, pointing towards the sun. I cannot hear *Them,* as their double-agent mics in their cell phones have not been picked up by my Stingray.

It is a little after 6:00 a.m., and the other graveyard maintenance engineers for the Seneca Indians bumble slowly into the gray fog known as an *Upstate* sunrise. Barbara and her coworkers would all be back at the casino fourteen (14) hours later in the day for their next eight (8) hour janitorial shift (earning a whopping forty-three dollars) ($43). Nonetheless, they wish each other sincerely a "Happy Mother's Day!"

Apart from this unlivable wage, trying to escape from Seneca gambling work is impossible for Barbara and her peers. They live within the poverty of Appalachia. But here on the Seneca Indian Nation Reservation, the Seneca OWN the land the town sits on. Whitey rents from the Seneca....

The Seneca were legislating and executing a disciplined white-devil gentrification from their ancient Great Hill and Western Door to America property. At the food store, in the parking lot, and in their cars at the drive-through, the Seneca Indians stared and schemed patiently in order to reverse the Indian Removal Act of 1830 and/or Barbara Dalton's forked tongue Manifest Destiny.

Barbara hangs out with the other maintenance engineers in the vacant Appalachian parking lot. Like in Albany, the sun doesn't rise here in the Southern Tier. The Empire's sun maybe appears as a gray-yellow blob, a green-gray booger, and/or a star out of rhythm and/or off key.

Dear Family Court, Good Reader, and Good Looker: I will paint the scene above with Barbara at dawn as People's Exhibit F. But I will draw out a large Pagan axe in her little hand because I swear to you

**People's Exhibit F — Barbara Dalton
at Dawn in the Casino Parking Lot**

all: looking through the right-side of my brain, I
can see the axe that Barbara grinds!

Sharon, a friend of Barbara, hands Barbara a white
carnation that she just retrieved from her car.
Sharon holds onto her own white carnation. They
stand there, seeming to pray to a Flower God or a
Mother's Day Goddess, but more likely they pray to
a male, man-made God.

Sharon says, "I'm heartbroken because I have not
seen my son in five (5) years." Sharon leans on
Barbara's rusted-out but at one point baby-blue
1976 Ford Pinto worth maybe three hundred dollars
($300). She exclaims, "If I just knew where he was,
I'd feel so much better."

Barbara thinks to herself but stays mum about her
son, Christopher, whom she won't talk to either.
But she knows where he is. It is the best place
for Chris, and not a "Christopher." Chris Dalton is
in the Empire State's Supermax Attica Prison. Barb
offers Sharon a Seneca cigarette (Employee discount
- $0.49 a pack). Sharon politely declines.

Chris is in Attica serving a sentence for raping
his female Appalachian neighbor. It's a barbaric
story with sordid and vulgar details that I will
spare this Honorable Court and Good Reader. Here
in Appalachia, rape has recently become something
the local District Attorney (DA) will prosecute.
So, Barbara tried to defend her rapist son and
in fact hired a fancy big lawyer from Albany who
charged her an eight-thousand-dollar ($8,000) up-
front retainer to defend her son of the charge of
rape. It was Barbara's life savings pittance and
mostly the inheritance her mother left her when she
died twenty-two (22) years ago in 1999. Barbara had
been saving the money as a college fund for her
children. After months of bad communication between
the Albany lawyer and Chris, Chris decided a week
before the trial to fire his lawyer and just plead

guilty to the charge of raping his neighbor. The money was not refunded, and Chris Dalton was sentenced to fifteen (15) years in Attica.

Barbara's eight-thousand-dollar ($8,000) college fund for her only son – for her sexy son – instead funded the sleazy Albany lawyer and his swinger girlfriend to vacation at Hedonism in Jamaica for a week.

Unfortunately, Chris Dalton's college education was in the showers of Attica, where Professor Bubba gave cum-dumpster-Chris his daily multi-choice quiz for eleven (11) years. In this dark, moldy, and sexually-transmitted-disease (STD) covered bathroom, Chris Dalton became enlightened with Professor Bubba's wise question: "Do you want to get raped like I *love* you or raped like I hate you?" Amazingly, Chris always answered Professor Bubba perfectly, earning himself an A+ every day and a degree from Attica Showers Community College (ASCC).

Barbara talks to Chris weekly and never speaks of his guilty plea of raping a woman. They only discussed the pleasantries of prison life such as the food, extracurricular activities, and the very gray weather. Barb prays for her son's soul, but Chris does not pray for himself or others because he does not know and/or want to know *love*, law, Christ, God, or the Empire. Chris, like the majority in Appalachia, only knows how to survive today. Tomorrow is up for grabs in Appalachia – tomorrow is a gamble.

Barbara's friend Sharon continues expressing her disbelief and disappointment with being estranged from her son. She holds her white carnation, using it as a motherly pointer:

"I'm not a whore," Sharon whines. In reality, her only high in life is being a tease or a skank. She continues, "I wish my son would *love* me, but his father is such a little-dick asshole that he'll never let that happen."

My exterior cameras zoom in. I can see Sharon tear-up. She says in a whisper to Barbara, "My son will never know how abusive his father was to me, so he will never understand me." Sharon, boiling up, violently throws her white carnation away onto a dirty, brown pile of snow. The lake-effect wind catches the white carnation, and it blows into a large, dark puddle or pond next to the snow. The carnation catches the wind, and its flower petals merrily float and navigate the parking lot lake.

I look at my fake white carnation from the *Gas Station Man*. It reminds me of the second letter I hold in my M-8888 satchel. It is an editorial written by my Grandmother Anna Jarvis for her local Philadelphia newspaper about white carnations. It also generally covers everything under the sun. The fake white carnation from the *Gas Station Man* has blossomed on my dashboard like a ship's figurehead warding off evil spirits and announcing my simple white carnation mission to all who cross my path and to even the illiterate.

As a backstory to my Grandmother's letter, I must tell you, Family Court and Dear Reader, that at the time she wrote this letter (1934), my grandmother was legally suing numerous "Christian Pirates," "Infringers," and "Charity Charlatans" for "Mother's Day" copyright and trademark infringement. Her editorial was titled:

"Dear *Expectant Mother Racket* — Reform Not Revenue!"

After establishing the white carnation flower as a symbol of motherly *love* back in 1908, my grandmother Anna Jarvis enjoyed respect for the motherly tradition that spread nationally and internationally. This respect for mothers created huge fortunes for the flower industry and the Flowers Transworld Delivery (FTD) company. The profits were vulgar, especially after colluding, monopolizing, and gouging the white carnation flower market. My grandmother lost her mind over the flower industry selling white carnations at a profit. She correctly claimed the flower industry was not just raising and price-fixing white carnations for their living and breathing mothers but profiteering even more by introducing the new red carnation for their dead mothers.

The *Red-Queen* was propped-up and paid back retro-actively in her absence, in her death, with a red carnation. This enabled all dead mothers with lists of debts unpaid and in arrears to come back from the grave and collect. Here is a *Red-Queen's jouissance* beyond death, and her orgasm. Here is the *Red-Queen's little death* - here is the Red Queen's reincarnation!

This pump and dump of Mother's Day as an Anti-War Holiday was destroying my grandmother. The monetization and commodification of my Granny's anti-child-abuse Holiday was killing her. My grandmother wrote in her Philadelphia editorial:

> Dear Phila, Dear City of Brotherly and Sisterly *Love*, Dearest Philadelphia and Respected Editors of the "Philadelphia Inquirer,"
>
> ***Your child is a Monster!***
>
> ***Your Expectant Mother Racket child is still borne!***
>
> ***Dear women all alone, including myself — let us reform our female ways as charity charlatans.***
>
> ***Let's take our tools back!***

Let's end our lame Hallmark attempts at
expressing our *love* for our mothers and write
a handwritten note to our mothers in our own
language. The dead carnation and rotten candy
are more for us than them.

And I am just as guilty. As a daughter on
Mother's Day, my pretty sentiment was the
empty candy box on my mother's living room
floor littered with glistening tinfoil wrappers from the chocolate sweets. My motherly
love has a stomachache that lasts a lifetime!

Dear women of Friendship — dear women of
Phila, let us pray to the same mother, let us
pray to the same Creator. Let us be a soldier
for Sophia, let us be a soldier for the divine
spark, a soldier who takes up arms against our
male creditors. Let's throw away our self-
aggrandizing carnations that wilt so fast.

These white carnations, these flowers — are
these the eyes of a man who does not adore
you? Oh, Diana and Marianne, oh Mary and
Eve, forget your sentimentalism, for we are
not debtors. I will create a badge for those
brave women who will fight against the murder
of our sons and daughters with their frivo-
lous wars and abstract debt.

Watch the insipid carnation gift for your
mother wither and die, curling in on itself
like an aging spinster. The mother who does
not protect her seedlings from war falls
apart, petal by petal with time.

Sincerely,

Anna Jarvis

My grandmother clearly expressed her mission. She
was obviously not scared of death. She was a woman

beyond the death-drive, taking back her tools, cap-
turing her *little Object A*. There is no fear of the
Other in her world; my grandmother was an artist /
a Creator / a Goddess.

I look over now at the plastic and white carnation
on the dashboard bow of my car. It bobbles like
a bobblehead. I need some fresh air and mistakenly open my window. The frigid dawn of Appalachia
rushes into my warm car. The casino dumpster stink
curdles my white carnation as fast as vanilla ice
cream melts on hot apple pie. My carnation is my
dying bowsprit, and her white petal sail is ripped
to shreds and blows in the wind. The cold air blows
my white carnation over and litters my dark inte-
rior with off-white petals that look like maggots.

I look up at Barbara. She still holds her white
carnation in a daze, and Sharon looks sadly at her
thrown flower drowning in a blacktop puddle. Their
motherly abuse makes for easy camaraderie. Barbara
seems to daydream for a moment. Her own husband is
a slimy, angry drunk and mean as spit.

Barbara then complains, "My children are always
being so ungrateful and such a pain in the ass."

Barb steps back and sips her burned coffee with
powdered milk floating on top and still not diluted
in a plastic Styrofoam cup. Barbara asks Sharon,
"What effect did your husband have on your family?"

The nondairy creamer forms a crust on her upper
lip which Barb licks, sucks, and crunches on with
her yellow and brownish, badly deteriorated teeth.
Barbara seems drugged on this High Fructose Corn
Syrup (HFCS) and loses her train of thought.

Barb takes a drag on her Seneca cigarette and in
a newfound rush of energy says, "Fuck 'em all...
They condemn me every day of my life." Small puffs
of smoke puff out of her small mouth with no lips.

Barbara concludes, "My family, my Elders have always and will always condemn me... but today, on Mother's Day — I say fuck 'em all, Sharon! Fuck 'em all!"

Barbara Dalton's *Fuck 'Em All* declaration of independence reminds me of Susan Dalton. Susan is Barb's youngest daughter who had just moved back home to Allegheny with her two (2) children. Barbara's house in Allegheny, according to Zillow (ZG), was worth around twenty-six thousand dollars ($26,000). Barbara's husband and Susan Dalton's father, William or Billy Dalton, was livid and caustic with any and every move Susan and/or her children / his grandchildren make. Besides the underlying immaturity and criminality of this Appalachian family, Billy Dalton, the man of the house, is an alcoholic. He was pissed because Susan was stealing half his beers from his daily Silver Bullet twenty-four (24) pack ($25.99). Susan, his daughter, had inherited the Dalton alcoholic gene, and she had been quenching and promoting that disease with grain alcohol and beers since she was thirteen (13) years old.

The disease of alcoholism is part of the Empire's biological warfare on Appalachia. Alcoholic warriors and patriots like Susan, her father, and her grandfather before that swapped out the American's and the Appalachian's "Good ole fight" with the "Good ole drunk." Billy Dalton with his innate wisdom of how to survive the next twenty-four (24) hours drunk has realized there could NOT be two Dalton drunks within the same house, under the same roof, within the overall square footage of six hundred and twenty feet (620 square feet). Barbara's home has transformed into a lonely and dark Appalachian bar with a television (TV) stuck on one (1) fuzzy channel.

Barbara wonders silently, yet at the same time consoles and nods in agreement with Sharon. But Barbara is worried about her own Appalachian insane asylum and ponders which member of her family will pass out first today on Mother's Day.... Will it be Bill or Susan? Her drunk daughter or abusive husband? Barb could watch her husband be hanged and quartered without shedding a tear. But Susan, who had just moved back home, was cut from the same oily and dirty Appalachian cloth that Barbara was cut from. So Susan's demise was also Barbara's breakdown.

Barbara has a nighttime routine: Barbara would spit a nasty phlegm ball on her husband at around nine forty-five *post meridiem* (9:45 p.m.) every night after he passed out on his La-Z-Boy (LZB) foldout recliner. But Barb would put Susan to bed with warm blankets and freshly fluffed, clean pillows. Barbara cherishes this post-Dalton Rehabilitation Center pass-out time. She looks at her sleeping daughter, Susan, with hope. This nighttime was one of the few times of peace in Barbara's Allegheny home.

And during this right-brain time, the thought of losing Susan makes the very old little lady in the back of her mind look up cautiously. The thought of not having a daughter – a friend – makes the hair on the back of Barbara's neck stir and stand. The thought of losing Susan makes the inside of Barbara's palms sweaty and her throat go dry. The thought of losing Susan is accurate but not *Real,* and it is part of Barb's *Other*.

And Barbara, instead of being self-aware and grounded, is lost in the poverty and blight of *Motherhood* and the *Expectant Mother Racket.* Barbara abuses her subconscious / her *Other,* herself, because Barbara is abused by her husband. In Appalachia, there is very little trickle-down economics but there are mountain ranges of trickle-down abuse. It's a "Family-Friendly" family game we all play in Appalachia.

Barbara's oldest daughter, Tracy, thirty-eight (38) years old, will certainly be talking to Barb

today by phone. Tracy was smart enough to leave
Allegheny immediately after high school. Tracy
lives in Manhattan and has a good job and is the
fierce Dalton warrior on the march. Tracy is a rare
diamond in the rough of *Upstate*.

Tracy is a lean girl and took her father's strong
physical characteristics, but she glides with her
mother's genteel Southern soul and constitution.
Barbara's life in poverty is the reason Tracy works
so hard *Downstate*: she wants to rescue her mother.

Barbara consoles and/or compensates her own
"Motherly Batting Average" (MBA) or her "Breeding
Batting Average" (BBA) with, "Well, one (1) good
kid out of three (3) is better than zero (0) out of
three (3)." And Barbara is right about her "Runts
Battered In" (RBI) and/or her "Humans Better-Off
Than Me" (HBTM) data to a point. Barbara prays for
Tracy's continued success, even though Barbara is
nervous that Tracy is cursed with the Dalton gene.
Tracy calls her mother before 9:00 a.m. every day
to keep the emotional juices flowing through their
telephonic apron string.

Tracy, like her mother, is psychologically paranoid
- perverse. They live on fear; they live on the
negative-amortized life, the neg-am jam life - the
NAJ life. They fear themselves, growth, and change
- they piss on the *Real*, do not talk about the
Other, and choose to know nothing about *Nothing*.

Chapter 10

6:45 A.M. - <u>MOTHER IS JUDGED BY PATRICK PILATES, OR, COMPLAINT #21-6154</u>

1   I'm back on the nicest street in Allegheny again,
2   Highland Avenue. I can see on my main computer
3   built into the Empire's Trooper car dashboard that
4   Madeline is dozing on her guest couch. She suddenly
5   awakes after hearing the side house door slam. Mad
6   instinctually knows this is Christa coming home
7   at daybreak. Maddy gets up in a huff, puts on her
8   robe, and scuttles downstairs to confront / welcome
9   her daughter strolling in at sunrise.
10
11 Madeline hears giggling and talking coming from the
12 kitchen and wonders if Christa is on her phone.
13 Madeline is happy to welcome Christa home and make
14 her breakfast. But Christa does not want to see
15 her mother, unless she needs a little "Allowance"
16 for her bank account. Christa never wants to see
17 her mother especially on Mother's Day. Christa has
18 brought home an old Allegheny boyfriend, Patrick
19 Pilates, whom Madeline enjoys very much, probably
20 too much.
21
22 Madeline and Patrick, or "Pilates" as he goes by,
23 have had a small and aspiring "Romantic" chick-lit
24

e-book narrative going on via their Snapchat (SNAP) direct messages (DM) for the last three (3) months. I will spare this Good Family Court, but Dear Reader, the prose is not *Romantic* literature that describes Pilates and Madeline. The problem is as old as Medusa, but now it's called Mothers I'd Like to Fuck (MILF).

Like Medusa, *Motherhood*, and now whoring mothers – these are man-made inventions for women's incarceration. Another white-devil problem, another small-white-dick (SWD) problem – destroying a woman – lighting her hair on fire with snakes and turning her into a feared monster because another man touched HIS woman. Maddy says her daughter is a thief, but Mad is fucking her daughter's boyfriend, Pilates... and Christa knows.

Patrick and Christa are groping each other in the kitchen when Madeline, bright-eyed and bushy-tailed, walks in on *Them* making out, playing grab-ass.

Madeline gasps a little. She is a little taken back because Pilates is hugging and squeezing Christa from behind, which is pushing her daughter up against her Italian refrigerator ($16,860) finished in custom ash wood to match the cabinets, which cost thirty thousand two hundred dollars ($30,200 – Installation Included). Christa giggles and gyrates her ass into Pilate's groin as ice from the dispenser spills onto the floor. Patrick Pilates licks Christa's neck and manhandles her breasts from underneath her blouse like a looter grabbing merchandise at a supermarket riot.

Madeline pretends not to notice any of this. Maddy hesitatingly says, "Ga-ga-goo-goo-good morning.."

Sheepishly, Pilates extracts himself from Christa's body. He backs up six (6) feet or so and puts his hands in his pockets. Pilates, standing tall, still erect, and at attention, says, "Good morning, Mrs. McHugh!"

Christa sighs disapprovingly in her mother's face, snapping and snarling, "What are you doing?" as the ice cubes continue to spill onto the travertine marble floor ($189 a square foot). Christa's ass still gyrates as if Pilate's hard cock were still there.

Madeline answers slowly like a scared and demented child, "I-I-I was up, and I-I-I thought I'd make you br-br-break-break-break...fast-fast."

Christa slaps back, "You're always up. Get the hell outta here!"

Christa lets that "Helicopter Mom"/ "Baby-Boomer Bimbo" bombshell fly, whiz, and echo across Madeline's bow and throughout their twelve-thousand-square-foot (12,000 sq. ft.) vacant McMansion. They all wait in silence for the emotional shrapnel to really infect and wound Christa's true mortal enemy - her mother. This momentary silence freezes everyone, and no one knows what to say as a domestic parasite settles into its host - the lap of luxury.

Madeline retreats to pleading, "I was just trying to make everyone happy! Happiness is the truth of life," looking at Pilates more than Christa. Maddy then very quickly gets on her knees and starts cleaning up the ice cube mess her daughter was making.

Pilates looks down and painfully smiles at Madeline on the floor practically washing his feet. Then Pilates scowls with that frat-boy grimace as if someone has a clamp on his dick and he kind of likes it. Mad, the *Red-Queen*, happily looks up to catch a glimpse of a Pilates with his dick in a honey-trap. Madeline enjoys this torture of *lover* and daughter at the same time. The triangulation of Pilates's male gaze looking for some easy pussy is complemented by Christa's kleptomaniac flare for throwing *loved* ones onto intimate fires.

"Can't you see I'm here with a friend? Ma-de-line?" Christa slowly brings the heavy black pillow closer to her mother's bloated white face. Christa starts to smother her mother once again by calling her mother by her first name in a slow, downbeat, overly pronounced, monosyllabic, punching-down manner.

"What are you doing... Ma-de-line?" Christa slowly twists and screws again. This child is a bully tyrant, and her mother is an innocent child of God about to be judged for execution / for crucifixion.

Christa has vocally devalued Madeline since she was a young teenager. Madeline, still on her knees and now at her daughter's feet, is unsuccessfully trying to pick up the melting ice cubes off the white marble floor. Madeline moves around her daughter as if she is a violent, mentally ill patient at an insane asylum. Maddy is the unfortunate nurse who changes the bedpan dutifully. At the same time, Maddy grabs at the ice cubes as they swim and squiggle away, laughing and melting like hooligans at the gallows pole or rubberneckers at a crucifixion.

Madeline answers her daughter Christa as if her daughter is really interested in her mother's life, "Oh, thanks for asking, Christa. I'm not up to much, a little needlework, and then I have to bring Hersey to the vet tomorrow. Hoi is coming over later, so I've got to...."

"No, no, not today, Ma-de-line!" Christa rudely interrupts, as Madeline tends to ramble on if not physically bridled / controlled. Christa crosses her arms and continues: "Right now in front of me — what are you doing? I'll give you a clue... you're annoying me! I'll ask you again before you go away. Let's see if the Me-Generation Mommy can answer a question that doesn't have the subject of 'Me' in it. What are you doing, Ma-de-line?" Christa slowly twists and screws Madeline's soul into the cold, dark earth again.

Madeline pleads again, "I'm just trying to make everyone happy. Doesn't everyone want the truth and happiness?"

Madeline is still on her knees, chasing and grasping at frantic, hysterical, and invisible ice cubes. As Madeline chases the ice cubes between Christa's feet, she also starts washing Christa's feet with her bloodshot, bleary eyes and proclaims, "I just want to make sure Mr. and Mrs. Homecoming 2021 and the King of the Mohawks are okay. You were out all night. Can I make the King and Queen of Allegheny breakfast?"

Christa sighs and huffs again in a disapproving fashion, looking down at her mother, who is still chasing the icy water puddles of ice cubes sliding across the white marble floor. She chuckles at her pathetic mother, still on her knees. Christa plays along mischievously, "Hey, Maddy, you got some of that Barabbas breakfast sausage? Pilates *loves* that Barabbas red meat."

Pilates squints in pain at Christa with a furrowed brow, shaking his head in disapproval, and mouths the words, "Fuck, Barabbas!"

But Pilates is gazing / glaring at his MILF. He seems perplexed with Madeline's idea of "Truth and happiness." Unseen by Madeline, Pilates mouths the words silently to Christa, "What is the truth?" shrugging his shoulders and opening his hands – asking the question with his body language.

Pilates then orates in a commanding voice to every-one, even to the unruly ice-cube crowd at his feet, and asks honestly: "Whom shall we dine with? Barabbas breakfast sausage or the 'Truth' at breakfast?"

Christa gives Pilates the middle finger. Madeline
is still on her hands and knees and is unable to
see behind the scenes or any of her incarcerator's
juvenile sign language. Pilates grabs his crotch
and points to the basement, smiling like a horny
toad.

Christa silently nods "Yes" to him with a big
smile. She speaks to her condemned mother in a
new, healthy, spritely tone inspired by Pilates's
keen political sense of the *truth* and happiness.
Christa, in her best Southern Appalachian accent,
says, "Aww, Ma, thanks anyways, but we'll pass on
the Barabbas breakfast sausage. We're gonna juust
waaatch a movie in the baaasement."

Madeline chomps down on the bait, on Christa's emotional hook, as she looks up from the floor at her
daughter in pure glee with this new, respectful
tone from Christa. Maddy sing-songs, "Okay, dear,
that sounds like fun; I'll get some corn for the
pop-corn-popper!"

Christa looks down at her mother and teasingly
says, as if in on the joke: "Hey, Maddy, I know I'm
the Homecoming Queen, but I heard you are the Queen
of Clean Kitchens!!!"

Madeline takes on the persona of a quiet martyr.
She answers solemnly, "I am today on this glorious
Mother's Day going to honor mothers and testify
to the truth. The truth is that those that know a
clean kitchen listen to me... and my clean kitchen
kingdom is from another world!"

Christa and Pilates are not listening and are already
halfway down the stairs into the basement (which
Pilates and Christa call the Fuck-Pit Coliseum).

Mad continues to unsuccessfully chase the slippery ice-cube puddles as they taunt, tease, and
chastise her with a chanting, escalating whisper:

"Crucify! Crucify! Crucify! Crucify! Crucify! Crucify! Crucify!"

Madeline regains her *Mother's Day Madness* composure after being Passover-ed and/or crucified to a cross. Mad, the luxurious mother, has been nailed to a cross. Luxury is hanging from a cross now, but she is still undaunted and yells down to Christa and Pilates, teasing *Them*, begging *Them*, and trying to appeal to *Them*: "And don't forget it's Mother's Day today!"

The popular thief and Pilates, with muddy shoes and unclean hands, swap spit and viciously French-kiss as they descend the basement staircase playing slinky grab-ass. They bounce off the staircase walls, scratching and staining the wallpaper that cost forty-five dollars ($45) a yard. They spill their drinks, staining the wall-to-wall carpet with their dirty feet as they descend into the deluxe, three-thousand-three-hundred-and-fifty (3,350) square-foot finished basement.

This underground loft of luxury with twelve (12) foot ceilings has an exercise room, a spa, a full bathroom, a small kitchen, a bedroom, an office, a game room, and a very large wood-paneled home theater with an antique popcorn concession stand. The basement – or the "Fuck-Pit Coliseum" as Christa and Pilates call it – cost around four hundred and forty-five thousand dollars ($445,000) to finish two (2) years ago, as Madeline wanted it "For the children." Her husband's accountant suggested he "Write it off" as an Empire State tax deduction under another "Home / Office" deduction.

After hearing Madeline's morning announcement, Pilates aggressively pulls away from Christa's sumptuous body and stutters, "Wha-wha-wha-what the hell did your mother just say? Did she say it was Mo-Mo-Moth-Moth-Mother's Day?"

Christa snorts, "I don't give a fuck," and pulls Patrick Pilates's pants down to his ankles to prevent him from running away.

Pilates looks at his TAG Heuer wristwatch ($3,499) and shrieks, "Holy shit! It is Mother's Day – I gotta go!"

Christa wrestles her man against the popcorn maker and by accident turns it on. Christa tempts Pilates, "Just wait, I want to show you the *truth*," as she fondles Pilates's hard cock and balls. Christa slowly slithers up and down Pilates's body like a lap-dancer and then slowly kisses his tight six-pack and pelvis. She pulls down his Versace designer underwear ($129) and slowly kisses the top of Patrick Pilates's pubes... Christa lightly kisses Pilates's cock and says, "I will teach you about the *truth*."

Pilates struggles to leave and attend to the necessary *Mother's Day Madness* of Hallmark-card shopping, flower shopping, and chocolate shopping, which has become synonymous with respect for *Motherhood*.

Patrick Pilates succumbs to the truth trial in the Fuck-Pit Coliseum and feels the truth start to boil and rise out of him. Twitching in ecstasy, I hear Pilates whimper in escalating tones: "I see the truth, I see the truth, I-I-I see the, I see, I-I see the truth...."

The popcorn popper starts popping in acapella harmony with Patrick Pilates. *Pop, pop, pop, I, I, I. See, pop, pop, pop, I, I, I. Pop, I, see the Pop, I see the pop, I see the truth. Pop, truth pop. Truth, pop, po. I, I, I, see, see, see, the, the, the, th, th, th, tru,tru,,tru, trut,trut,truth,truth.*

Patrick Pilates exclaims in heightened and peaceful orgasmic relief as if enlightened and transcended, "Aagh yes, oh yes... I see it now... the motherfucking truth...."

But right then, Pilates suddenly snaps out of this eros trance and implores, "Stop, stop, stop, Christa.... This is not the truth - I gotta go shopping for my Mom! It's Mother's Day, for God's sake!"

Pilates pulls away from Christa's embrace and pleads, "I also gotta cook up some of that Barabbas breakfast sausage. My Mom *loves* that true Barabbas meat on Mother's Day." Pilates declares and concludes, "Sorry, I choose Mother Barabbas instead of you, Christa."

Pilates runs up the Fuck-Pit Coliseum stairs, pulling up his pants.

Christa slumps down to the floor in a dejected manner. Christa, all alone now, looks sad and disappointed for a moment and then seems to get angry. Christa starts eating popcorn in the large, dark, and subterranean vacant space. Christa is thinking very hard about something... planning something... maybe revenge, or maybe a religion.

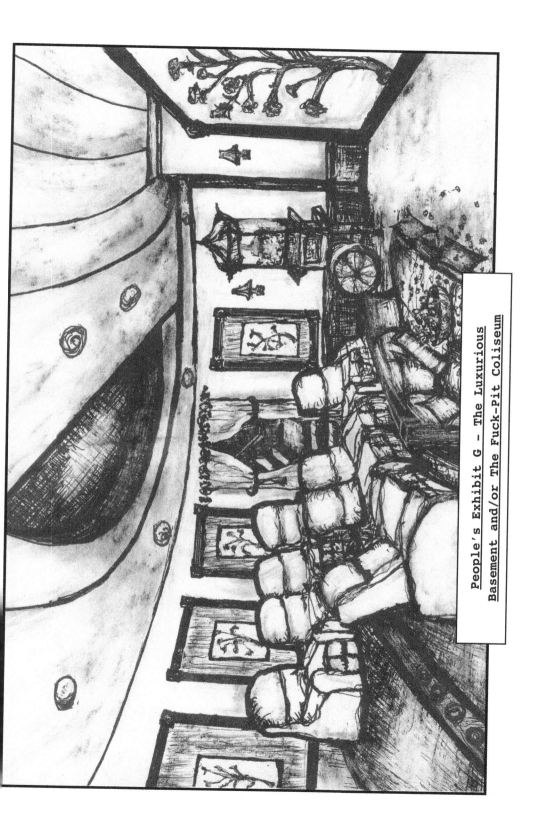

People's Exhibit G — The Luxurious
Basement and/or The Fuck-Pit Coliseum

Chapter 11

7:57 A.M. - MOTHER IS SCOURGED, AND A CROWN OF THORNS IS PUT ON HER HEAD, OR, COMPLAINT #21-4532

I have driven approximately two (2) miles down towards the river and railroad tracks to Complaint #21-4532's house. I'm looking for a parking spot, but Dam Road is lined with rusted-out, half-dead automobiles. The Allegheny townie with his snow-plow has not been down here on Dam Road yet – poverty is not respected. The snow is only two (2) inches deep, but the middle of the road is becoming a small pond. Two (2) young teenage hooligans with skull masks and revved-up all terrain vehicles (ATV) keep running through the puddle. A younger child, a redheaded little maniac sits on top of a rusted wreck cheering *Them* on as they try to spray him with their trikes' wave or wake arc of puddle water.

The wrong side of the tracks in Allegheny reminds me of Northern Ireland during the "Troubles." The ten- to twelve- (10-12) year-old maniac on top of the car with Heat-Miser-red-hair gets pissed after being splashed too much. He whirls around with a .22-caliber rifle or a large BB gun. He pretends to shoot his trike buddies as they pass, and I feel the action heat up! I feel at home here... definitely 1970s Appalachia, around the bend from 1980s Belfast.

The houses on Dam Road look like English (UK) Empire row housing in Birmingham or Manchester, England, but these houses have been Americanized and built out of wood instead of brick or concrete. The houses are all mashed together into some communist labor ghetto.

Allegheny reminds me of a Pennsylvania coal town on the skids. Architecturally, there is no roof gable differentiation: roofs are shared like broken crutches or sistered bridges to uphold a Pennstucky utopia within poverty. The patios — the best seat in the house – are shared with neighbors' work trucks and abandoned boats. Balconies are recycling centers for appliances, bottles, glass, and rotten wood lumber. The same window has different color shutters and/or opposing sports flags showing the struggle or rivalry in a split state.

Downstate Philadelphia Eagles pennants fly proudly in the top of a double-hung window. But on the bottom, a Pittsburgh Steelers blanket is stapled cock-eyed, warning everyone, "This is Steeler Country!" Architecture in poverty clearly shows America's schizophrenic and/or split-personality socioeconomic society.

Third-world Appalachian architecture: there are two (2) doors, where there should be one (1). The front door is an abandoned, dusty, dead door where PennySavers and newspapers in colorful bags collect. Only the side door is used in poverty, and curb appeal is a foreign language. In poverty, there are boarded-up windows on the factories and warehouses that hide the sunshine. Here in the dark – that used to be the industrious American middle class – is where there used to be many clean windows that let sunshine inside. A building needs sunshine in order to grow, but not here in poverty, Appalachia. Poverty boards up and bricks up windows where there should be sunshine.

Here in this third-world, white-trash ghetto, there are the ongoing "Parking Wars" you may have heard of. Parking in crowded Appalachia is on the level of male animals competing with breeding dances to show off their good masculine genes via their deluxe parking. Autoerotic males and females fight in order to win the right to park. Parking power is on the level of hand-to-hand combat in Appalachia. Guerrilla warfare with armed conflicts, booby-traps, and crude intimidation was the military sci-ence. Psychological operations such as tire rims with sticks as blockades. Signs reading "Park Here and DIE!!" or "No U-Turn, Faggot!" is the *modus operandi / method of operation* in poverty, America. This *Intelligence* works on the level of the prison gangs that rule this Appalachian roost.

This Allegheny architecture shows no individualism or freedom. It is similar to the *Charity Soldier* fashion. This *Charity Soldier* architecture unasham-edly shows a communist police-state stuck in a third-word prison dilemma.

The dilemma of *Us* coming from the wrong side of the railroad tracks compared to *Them*. Coming from the wrong side of the river, the wrong side of town. You know where... we discussed this earlier. Dear Reader and Honorable Family Court, remember where everything is wrong. Whereville? Yes, exactly.

Black soot coal dust coats everything in Appalachian daydreams and nightmares for *Us.* Dinge in every color and dinge in every shade are what the houses are painted by *Us.* The dinge comes from a poi-sonous mine fire we cannot extinguish. It burns in our souls twenty-four (24) hours, seven (7) days, and three hundred and sixty-five (365) days a year.

But, for *Them*, the smokestacks and coal-breakers are trophies on our horizons that keep on crushing it / keep on killing it for eternity.

Is it Jesus or the Federal Reserve who stands up for the poor the best? Who said: "We will always have the poor?" It certainly wasn't the socialist Nordic countries of Europe who are the happiest Vikings in the world. The Nordics know the aliens – they know *Them*.

My undercover cop car spooks the teenage hooligans who think there is going to be some kind of raid. In Sandinista and Kabul, the children are paid scouts sending *Intel* to the "Bad guys." Children of Bad-guys and/or Bad-gals have very little choice in this tribal war. The redheaded sniper-in-training and his skull-boy friends on trikes disappear along the wood line. My Empire cop-car is worth more than this entire block of houses. Ten (10) houses on Dam Road times the average price of a house on Dam Road is $18,349 x 10 = $183,490. An Empire State cop-car costs one-hundred-ninety-five-thou-sand ($195,000) from local GOP Ford (F) dealer in the Albany Capital. My Empire State car crawls along Dam Road looking for the target Dalton house and has at least a tenfold advantage.

I spot the Dalton house amidst a front lawn that looks like an abandoned demolition derby from the 1970s crossed with Burning Man "Sculpture Art." These Appalachian hippy-pirates were definitely leaving more than a trace. The white-trash Appalachian is bloated... they are a brown skid-stain on whitey-tighty America.

I park down the road a bit and settle in. I turn on my Stingray and can hear those three (3) children scouts in the woods talking on their cell phones. The children are panting, screaming — no order, just chaos and more yelling — one yelling over the other. No order, no hierarchy, just desperate screaming at each other, struggling for power. The children talk to deadbeat Big Daddy, Uncle Fuck-Up, and/or both. These Appalachian rats are in a predator's trap. Satellites lock into longitude and then get cocked into latitude and then, on a black-and-white screen — in another world — puff... you're a satellite bug-splat — yesterday's news. It sounds like Uncle Fuck-up and/or Big Daddy are running a meth-lab somewhere around here. I cannot be bothered. The Empire has *Them* on their Global Positioning System (GPS). Time is not on their side... time does not tell time anymore; time tells me Nothing... time is a mathematical matrix meant to confuse.

Regardless, these tough "Allegheny men" will surely celebrate in the woods tonight that they beat "The Man" and/or "The Empire." These men will dance around a fire with whiskey and drugs, just as their fathers, grandfathers, and past generations have. They won't invite their children or women in camaraderie or partnership. These demented men will dance around the fire and beat each other until they get bored. Then they will go home to their disgusting homes / double-wide trailers and beat their wives, girlfriends, and stray children - demanding more "Respect" because "The Man" and/or "The Empire" was fooled by their slick criminal tricks today.

But using children as scouts is ignoble for warriors, and these red-state rednecks mooching within a blue-state do not understand that the Empire savors its time. It is the Empire's time in 2021 — and not our time.

Can you hear time tick and tock? Tick... tock... tick... tock.... Chronos spins the zodiac wheel of time, and Cronus with his scythe cuts the seasons harvest. Can you hear Einstein time? It's half past a wormhole. Tick... tock... tick... tock.... Can you hear Quantum Entanglement time? It's spooky.... Can you hear Fibonacci time? It sounds like the sum of the past. Tick... tock... tick... tock.... Can you hear Grandmother Paradox time? It sounds like infanticide: crying babies being tortured and killed. Tick... tock... tick... tock....

Oh, can you hear that? Is that Kilgore Trout bazooka time? Or is it Kurt Vonnegut's "Time Quake" time? A time when you were sick, but you're okay now, and there is A LOT of work to be done. Can you hear remote viewing (RV) time? It sounds like Montauk time – heavy rocks rolling underwater. Yes, I sat in the Montauk chair – I'm a Montauk girl. Tick... tock... tick... tock.... Maybe it's becoming Sumerian time and not Empire time? Sophia time? Divine spark time? Inanna / Enki time?

Nonetheless, I log into my computer. My screens pick up the optics in Barbara Dalton's house. She is home from work now and waiting for her husband and grandchildren to wake up. She is relaxing, having a smoke in her basement. The grandchildren are not allowed in the small earthen basement that measures around twelve (12) feet by fifteen (15) feet, making the basement one hundred and eighty (180) square feet. The ceiling is only about five (5) feet high, so it is not really a small basement but a large crawl space. Barbara's earthen crawl space room is accessed by a rickety staircase with missing steps. The basement has boarded-up windows. It is lit with a swinging, exposed light bulb that constantly sways, making it feel like you are in the hull of a boat during a storm. The crumbling fieldstone foundation is hidden by numerous old boilers and water heaters knocked over and in disarray. There is no natural light in Barb's crawl space. It smells like moldy ghosts; it smells like brown and gray dead bodies having a smoke break.

Barbara would say to her grandchildren, "I don't want to harm you with my stupid smoking habit, so never come downstairs to the basement. Never!"

The basement's earthen floor is not brown like dirt, but sooty gray with little yellow-orange specks because so many cigarette butts had been planted in this dirt. Barb's basement is a two-hundred square foot (200') ashtray that smokers could sit in.

Barbara's basement staircase is creaky, wobbling, and treacherous. It leads to nothing better upstairs. To cross this staircase, one takes on the possibility of it collapsing and breaking one's neck. That is the fun of the self-destructive Appalachian life — the thrill of doing more damage is just a hootenanny away.

This crawlspace is where Barbara feels most comfortable in life. A safe space, a room with a lock, allowances and an income of much less than Virginia Woolf's suggestion in 1930 of forty thousand dollars ($40,000) a year. Barbara thinks smoking in the basement is respectful to her grandchildren she raises because now she was "not smoking in the house."

Barbara also enjoys looking at her husband's "Sea of Green" cannabis Sativa plants growing under his sodium-halide light farther back in a smaller closet. Barb enjoys the smell of the Indica and Sativa, a pure, fresh, green elixir. It is a double-whammy green high of THC and another green high of six thousand ($6,000) dollars in annual income. Three harvest cycles net Bill Dalton around two thousand ($2,000) dollars each harvest. Barbara rolls her own cigarette with Seneca Indian tobacco and lightly pruned flowers from her husband's Northern Light and Kush garden.

Even though Barbara Dalton has taken precautions and thinks constantly and endlessly about how to protect her children and grandchildren, she does not. Barbara has no more DNA random-access-memory (RAM). Barb has run dry on DNA RAM.

The cigarette smoke and ganja smoke wafts up between the floorboards of Barbara's dilapidated one-hundred (100) year-old house. It creates a kind of Appalachian fog or smog in the children's bedroom upstairs. Their bedroom is in the unfinished attic. And just like in the Hudson Valley outside Mr. Appleton's window, there are fluffy / smoky patches of white cotton candy in the hills and valleys. Well, here in Barbara's house, the smoky patches float around Craig and Diana's bedroom. This Appalachian smog is known as asthma, cancer, and/or parental child abuse. It's a wet affair, social engineering, soft-core eugenics, and/or self-help genocide.

The smoking rat hole Barbara Dalton calls a basement is, in turn, the grandchildren's soft-core eugenics room because, almost two (2) years ago, Barbara's daughter, Susan, lost custody of her two (2) children. The Empire State Family Court took *Them* away after deeming Susan Dalton an unfit mother. That Family Court Case (#19-3886) started after Susan's children crawled out a window onto the second-story roof of their Section 8 housing and started screaming for help!

"Help, help," the little ones screamed. "Our mother has locked *Us* in our room. We can't get out! Help!!! Helllppp!! Heeelllppp!!!!"

The neighbors called the Allegheny police, and the police found Susan passed out from drugs and alcohol with her African American boyfriend, who was not the father of either child. Both adults were arrested for drug possession and endangering the welfare of Susan's children and two (2) other children (locked in another room). Susan and her boyfriend told the police they were "Babysitting," but it turns out they were "Baby-killing."

The Empire State judge gave Susan a choice of getting a job or going to jail: Susan chose to go to jail, so Grandma Barbara Dalton got custody of her grandchildren, Craig and Diana.

They are good, innocent children at five (5) and nine (9), but nonetheless, the statistical odds are not in their favor. That the innocent children will amount to anything is doubtful, with both their parents in Attica State Prison. The children are taunted and shunned in school, and it's not just their chronic lice and flea problem the Allegheny school nurse has to deal with. With both parents in jail and with the alcoholic / addict gene in their bloodstream, they most likely will be joining their parents at Attica State Prison. Only money and *Intelligence* can save an innocent child, and no one can afford to save the Dalton children in Allegheny.

Barbara Dalton pulls on her spliff and enjoys the silence before her house erupts into full-blown Dalton Appalachia and/or the Dalton Rehabilitation Center and/or the Dalton Nursing Home, and/or the Dalton Metal Recycling, and/or the Dalton Automotive Repair and/or most important... in Appalachian terms: The Dalton Motor-Cross Raceway!

But for now, Barbara wonders to herself about her oldest daughter, Tracy, and how she is doing in the big *Downstate* city. Barb looks forward to her daily phone call with Tracy in an hour or so. Mother's Day is just another Sunday workday for the Seneca Indians (Barbara's employer) and the nonchalant / easily forgotten Sunday Holiday is similar for worhkaholic Manhattanites like her daughter Tracy.

Tracy is the cream of Barbara's motherly crop, and Barbara often admitted jokingly after raising Tracy that she kind of "Got tired of the whole mom thing." Barb taught Tracy to read and write at an early age. But when the other two children – Susan and Christopher – came around, Barb was more inter-ested in her lost youth, which resulted in a lot of drinking and smoking during pregnancy and after childbirth.

Christopher, her rapist son, was born slightly "Dry" in 1984. Barbara would jokingly exclaim to anyone who would listen that her water broke during one of her many popular house parties. Everyone at her house at the time was too drunk or stoned and couldn't drive her to the hospital. Barbara waited for her husband's friend to sober up for a few hours while she finished a few loads of laundry that had been lying around for a few weeks. Barb's sexy son was born slightly dead of dehydration and malnutrition in her womb.

Barbara's third child, Susan, was born about a year later, and she had tetrahydrocannabinol (THC), cocaine, methamphetamine, barbiturates, and Milwaukee's Best coaxing through her veins before she saw the light of day. Susan's blood alcohol content (BAC) at birth enabled her to be the first birthed-while-intoxicated (BWI) child in Allegheny. This is child abuse.

Neither Chris nor Susan received personal reading or writing lessons as Tracy did, and therefore, they were both drug addicts and in prison by the time they were sixteen (16). Tracy, the oldest daughter, in contrast, was the star pupil of Allegheny ele- mentary and high schools. Tracy left Appalachia on the first bus out of town after graduation. She went to the Big-Apple Empire city in order to (like me) possibly evolve past the negative amortized life, the NAJ life, the Devil's Island poverty life, oth- erwise known as the Appalachia American life.

Even with the reading lessons from Mom, Barbara could not protect her shiny diamond, Tracy, from being scratched, dulled, and dragged down by the scumbags of New York City. Barbara's fourteen (14) karat-diamond daughter had been baited and switched while she was looking for her little *Object A*.

Barbara imagines that Tracy, her diamond in the rough from the Southern Tier, would be very success- ful monetarily and would come back to Appalachia and rescue her. Barbara didn't care about Tracy's struggles in life because she had too many thorns in her own side already. Thinking about her other children – her bad ones – her son, Chris... or her youngest daughter, Susan... was too painful. The two youngest children made Barbara grind her teeth as she slept. Barbara massages the dull pain in her jaw from all the teeth-grinding. Barbara doesn't grin and bear it. She grinds and bears it. Despite it all, Barbara opens her Bible, pulls on her spliff, and blows O-ringlets into the fogged- out crawl space in a fun-loving way.

The ringlets widen into a hat or wreath of smoke that sits on Barbara's head. On my black-and-white pixelated screen, an interference or frequency starts to scramble my visual. Dear Family Court and Good Reader: I swear I almost see a smoky and spiky crown of thorns upon Barbara's head. The crown of thorns are from another world – an underwater world. And Barbara looks like a strange fish with a crown of thorns blowing air bubbles into the little aquarium basement she lives in. I'm starting to see too much.

The interference dissipates on my screens, and I can see the self-righteous Barbara as she flips through her large Bible that has a "Fuck You" sticker on the back in the shape of a fist with a middle finger extended upwards, insinuating, I suppose, her *Fuck You* Judeo-Christian religion. Even though I can see Barbara here in her crawl space, all I can picture is Barbara sitting on the toilet and hiding from her Elders back at the Seneca casino. She reads her Bible in peace on the toilet with her feet up so her Seneca Elders won't find her. This is a beauti- ful picture for you, Family Court, Good Reader, and Good Looker. I will paint with watercolors in every shade of black, white, and gray – and draw it out. I

People's Exhibit H –
Reading the Bible in Whitey's Toilet

will illustrate it for you in our universal visual
language. You will see and feel my *Intel* within the
right side of your brain in people's Exhibit H.

Barb's *Fuck You* religion doesn't bank with the
Bank of England or The Federal Reserve, so Barb
keeps her savings and cash money in the Seneca
Indian Employee's Pension Fund Bank Account. Barb
is praying to make it to retirement and/or salvation in three (3) years so she, too, can also leave
the poverty of Appalachia. Tracy, her one (1) good
child out of three (3) children, is Barb's ticket
to that salvation.

Chapter 12

9:08 A.M. - <u>MOTHER TAKES UP THE VEIL OF MADELINE, OR, COMPLAINT #21-6154</u>

I drive back to my stakeout on Highland Avenue - Complaint #21-6154. My laptop screens are up, and I am back in exu-burbia where driveways with twelve (12) foot-high driveway gates (like a person's shoes) tells *Intel* everything you need to know about who is inside.

Here on Highland Avenue, the gates have live cameras, mirrors, and passwords for military-grade security. Madeline's gate is landscaped with dark mulch that matches the twelve (12) foot black steel walls. The iron gates have two (2) cameras symmetrically hung dimensionally like gargoyles at eleven (11:00) o'clock and two (2:00) o'clock. The cameras hang like religious guilt. The beauty of luxury in exu-burbia where Very Important People (VIP) and/ or rich white trash very easily make more than a quarter-mill ($250,000) annually. Flowers sprout from her garden next to stone columns fit for a Viking *Red-Queen*. These gated McMansions all look like third-world compounds in Nicaragua or Markazi. At these large gates, digital arms reach out with

"Passcode-Only Entrance" while barbed-wire elec-
trified fences encircle everyone's property.

On my screens, I see Madeline waving goodbye to her
husband from the kitchen window as he pulls away.
Mr. McHugh yells out of his Mercedes Convertible
S-Class ($154,000) car window, "I'm going to do
errands."

Mr. McHugh gives Madeline one of his infamous
"McHugh Winks" that says way too much. Maddy is
waving her hand goodbye with a red carnation, and
she seems to be really annoyed.

Hoi-Noi enters the kitchen where Madeline is still
waving. She looks at the Mother's Day card, chocolates, and a bouquet of flowers that Mr. McHugh
has just given Madeline. Hoi-Noi touches the red
carnations and seems to be confused. She wonders
silently why the flowers are red carnations. Hoi-
Noi looks at Madeline numerous times in a nervous,
"Oh, shit, this white-devil lady is about to freak
out," manner. Hoi-Noi knows that Madeline knows
the difference between a white carnation and a
red carnation. Madeline's adulterous husband has
just given his wife and the mother of his three (3)
daughters a bouquet of flowers for a dead mother.

Hoi-Noi says, "Wow, this is such a well written
Mother's Day card – you should be so happy."

Madeline is not facing Hoi-Noi. She is closing the
open window and says nothing. Then Hoi-Noi starts
to say, "And these flowers..." But she is cut off
as Madeline whirls around, screaming bloody murder.

Mad is now a darker shade of her red carnations,
and she screams. She squeals, "Flowers? Hoi-Noi?
Flowers? Are you kidding me – these supermarket
flowers from last week are for a dead mother, Hoi-
Noi! A dead mother?! Don't you understand what
that perverted man with a little dick and a huge,

inflated ego – and bank account to match ~ is doing to me? Hoi-Noi, are you present? Hello, Hoi-Noi? He's profiting from me by entrapping me and his children. He just drove off on Mother's Day to fuck one of his kept whores. Whose side are you on, good woman? Don't you see my husband hurts me and his children with this vulgar and obscene behavior?"

Maddy looks at Hoi Noi, who doesn't completely understand Mad linguistically, but she completely understands Madeline emotionally and humanely. Hoi-Noi unfortunately does not project this with her body language, and so Mad gets pissed and dismisses her only friend in our world rudely by saying, "Oh, God... get the hell out of my kitchen, you dumb maid!!"

Hoi-Noi exits the kitchen as Mad continues to end-lessly and needlessly tidy up her ridiculously sized kitchen, which is about the average size of an entire house in America (fifteen hundred / 1,500 square feet).

It is a typical, gray morning in Appalachia, the Middle East, or Central America — a commu-nist police-state day, a rigged day, a Negative-Amortized (Neg-Am) Jam day. An *Us* and *Them* day. A haves and have-nots Empire day, a control-fraud day. In impoverished third-worlds, the weather is always the same: gray, humid, and stagnant. One cannot tell if the gray time of the day is nine (9:00) *ante meridiem* (a.m.), or six (6:00) *post meridiem* (p.m.). And no one seems to care. A long *Upstate* pea-soup day filled and smeared with gruel-ing humidity or bleak, bone-cracking ice. This gray-green, pea-soup day is the metaphysical weather of *Up-State* in Anywhere, America. This weather turns everyone here gray, greasy, and grumpy – the three (3) Gs of poverty. A third-world day. Come back in a century (100 years), and it's the same day. A scorched earth and blackened day... for poverty and/or luxury – it's all discontent.

I call in to the local Allegheny police department to trail Mr. McHugh, a.k.a. "Errand Boy." I suspect he is headed to one of his three (3) extramarital affairs. When he waved to Madeline, giving her that smarmy, adulterous smirk, it made me really angry. We have globally positioned McHugh as a child abuser and/or a person of interest (POI) physically and financially into the matrix for the last two (2) months and have found rhythms of strange movement and extended stays.

First, there was his purchase for his African American secretary of a condo ($255,000) near his family's business office. Next, there was the purchase of the nice house ($425,000) for an old high school sweetheart a few towns north with a Caucasian son who looks very much like Mr. McHugh. Lastly, there was the female teenager recipient of the "McHugh's Young Women Scholarship Award 2020" (MYWSA) ($382,000) to attend the local Jesuit all-girls private school for four (4) years after "Interning" at the McHugh business for two (2) months.

The Appalachian spring on this Mother's Day morning has not yet arrived. The mud season / frost-heave explosion is the current talk at the local Allegheny Diner where I stopped in before this stakeout. Mud-swallowed cars, mud-swallowed roads, and, as always, swallowed people are the hot topics this Mother's Day breakfast at the Allegheny Diner.

The gray intellectual stagnation of *Upstate* "Anywhere" is visible when looking at her citizens. The telltale sign of abused citizens in any Empire is their disingenuous faces. Their formless faces are a shocking punch. The flabby and fleshy frame is the second punch. This one-two punch is followed with a hook to one's Appalachian nose as acrid smoke from your neighbor's burn-pit wafts melting plastic into your house. The carcinogens are carried on a breeze from the rednecks down the road, burning themselves alive. Burning their trash not because it saves money and/or it's economical, but because making everyone sick around *Them* makes *Them* feel alive and positive. Even here on Madeline's luxurious street, the nicest one in Allegheny, one can smell the smoldering plastic melting on a wet log. *Us* has come to *Them*.

And even the morning after, the smoldering firepit glows with smoking unpaid bills and dirty diapers. The stench of poverty comes seething up from Dam Road and sits like dark, baggy eyes and furrowed brows over even the wealthiest faces of the Empire.

As I drive away from the Diner, through the morning crowds of Allegheny as they avoid their dead Main Street. They go to the box-stores that are designed for cars, trucks, and robots more than human beings. The lame and giddy citizens drive / dance and/ or mill about the box-store franchises... while their cars idle in the "Drive-Throughs." The citizens have an air of arrogance about how "American" they are. These rural metrosexuals and cosmopolitan Appalachians are smiling in their newly leased eighty thousand ($80,000) dollar cars that they cannot afford, yet the Empire who controls lending standards has said they can afford it. The crisis of mathesis is child abuse.

Appalachians these days remind me of the Cargo Tribes or the James Bond Tribe that I encountered near Guam. When I was an Air Force *Intelligence* operative-in-training, I had to do my jungle Survival, Evasion, Resistance, and Escape (SERE) course. I was a female *Intelligence* officer playing "Connie Bond." The big joke at Andersen Air Force Base (AFB) was about me, M-8888 and/or Lieutenant Munda, and how I was the new "Cargo Goddess" for the local indigenous people.

The natives worshipped the Air Force cargo ships and "James Bond" in particular because an American service man from World War II named James Bond and/

or who called himself "James Bond" helped these indigenous tribes. Since then, the native tribes have prayed to their "God" - "James Bond" — to return with more cargo supplies from America like, guns, televisions, and chocolate candy. We also brought the local natives water, Coca-Cola, Meals Ready to Eat (MRE), and other Western Psych-Ops propaganda. As a good mother or imperialist, we "*Love*" and/or "Infiltrate" the tribes in order to brainwash *Them* with commodity fetishes and *Gift-love*. The James Bond native tribe ceremony for our arrival of the C-130 cargo planes to their island was humbling — they built *Us* an airstrip out of colorful flowers!

As we landed our C-130 planes onto the remote Polynesian island, the "James Bonders" performed barefoot military parades with magical fake guns made of bamboo shoots. The airstrip was lined with the full spectrum of colors in a cockeyed and slanted fashion, and there was no centerline or flare path. The *James Bonders'* uniforms were Salvation Army donations mixed with ragtag camouflage uniforms left behind after World War II. This Salvation Army fashion is worn in all third-world police states - including Allegheny.

This desperate and inebriating fashion mixes meta-physically well with the fact that the whole island is drugged and drunk on their local drug: kava. It's similar to the way all of Appalachia is drugged and drunk on opioids (heroin), antidepressants, and alcohol. Likewise, the natives from Guam looked like the customers in the Allegheny "Dollar Store" this morning because they both fashion themselves with militaristic camouflage and Salvation Army finds that produce this "Charity-Soldier" third-world fashion.

The *Charity-Soldier* child in Markazi, Managua, or Allegheny wears khaki POLO (RL) linen shorts by Ralph Lauren (Ralph Lipschitz) which mixed nicely with his NIKE (NKE) "Just Do It" T-shirt. The ninety-pound (90-lb.) child holds a fifty-three-pound (53-lb.) Gattling gun currently made by General Electric (GE) and smiles happily. This is not charity. This is child abuse.

The Appalachians, like the *James Bonders*, line up politely and professionally at our military base or their favorite "Franken-Food Franchise" (FFF) to get their methadone candy. Both tribes think they have reached Nirvana, Xanadu, El Dorado, and/or Heaven as the biological and chemical warfare settles into their vital organs and brain. Both tribes are "Feeling American," but both are now genetically modified organisms (GMO) waiting in vain for their Cargo God or their "Capital God." They wait with dizziness, indigestion, and bloated stomachs as the poison of America – high-fructose corn syrup (HFCS)– makes the *James Bonders* sick and disabled. The *James Bonders* wait for their remedy, the proton-pump-inhibitors (PPI) in vain. The natives pray to their imaginary Cargo God for a miracle to calm their poisoned stomachs.

The Appalachian Franken-Food Franchises (FFF) are huddled strategically around the State and Federal Highway entrances and exits. These FFFs with gas stations are parasites for the human host. These FFFs with gas are like tattoo parlors and titty bars around a Navy Yard, scalping the sailor's pittance before he dies a lonely sailor's death at sea. The Throughway entrance and exits are monetarily rabid, even though our Main Streets are vacant ghost towns.

Instead, "Main Street," Appalachia, is lined with non-profits to help the enslaved Empire citizens in Appalachia stay incarcerated, uneducated, unenlightened, in the dark, and, as taught by their Empire Elders, to never ask: "Why, where, when, how, and/or who?" Global news is the new local news that has more sports and entertainment in the "News" than news.

In third-world countries functioning as feudal Empires, *Upstate*, America, and/or Appalachia, *"No news here – please move along"* is the only local news. The only global news in the Empire is: "No news – is good news." That's because in the Empire, bribery is not bribery, extortion is not extortion, and corruption is not corruption. Smoke-and-mirror news is the only news. Ben Franklin was right about the press being the necessary fourth (4th) State. But the press these days in the Empire is "Sponsored Content." They are a fraud, a treason, and all Main Stream Media (MSM) is nothing but yellow journalism in 2021.

The politicians who sponsor this yellow journalism are traitors to Americans, and treason is a capital offense. These politicians killed middle-class America from Chicago to Massachusetts, and then down the Appalachian Trail all the way to Alabama and Florida for the last eighty (80) years. Appalachian NAJ towns are now a tax write-off for global money-changers (*Them*). While *Us* – cosmopolitan rednecks – preen, dance, prance, and poison ourselves with biological and chemical (BC) warfare.

A drive-through Appalachian NAJ town is easy to locate. If the largest monetary budget in your zip code is your school district budget, then your children are educationally abused. That's because your tax-base should not be a NON-PROFIT educational agency for the children. It should be a FOR-PROFIT corporation churning out ten times (10x) that educational budget in order to pay the town's citizens a livable wage. Instead, these drive-through NAJ towns have a negative Gross Domestic Product (GDP) and survive as "Charity Towns" and/ or Welfare Queen Towns.

In drive-through Appalachia, the yellow-and-black

school buses idle and lumber along as prison ships
with no sails, transporting the children / pris-
oners-in-training to their school / prework. These
pompous parades of flashing lights and square-
dancing are for the citizens of the Empire and
Appalachia to feel morally superior because they
are politely killing their children.

But the real crime of treason comes in the "Help"
for third-world countries and Appalachia. The
pork-barreled Superfund or corrupt United Nations
International Monetary Fund (IMF) budget is corrupt. Money tries to fix the poison, remedy the
problem — the *Us / Them* problem — but it only
divides *Us* more.

In 2021, slush funds of charity (dirty debt) are
primed and pour in for Appalachia, Afghanistan, and
Managua. We are ripe for investments from private,
dark pools of money from the Federal Reserve and
Venture Capitalists (VC). We bury our children in
debt because Empire loyalists / royalists have no
one else to "Help" and/or deceive except our own
children.

The third-world is not reaching up to America for
help; America's innocent children are being pulled
down into the third-world. This is dark-pool social
engineering, this is banking-down with debt, this
is betting against our children. This is child
abuse.

I've driven back to Highland Avenue, and I'm looking at my screens. I see Madeline looking at her two
daughters (Michelle and Christa) and looking very
excited for it to be Mother's Day. But her oldest,
Margaret and/or Marge, is not coming home. Marge
is working hard in Manhattan to correct all of
Madeline's past mistakes and misfortunes with her
dutiful daughterly obedience as a Madeline double
— a Mad double. Margaret was raised to be another

country-club, stay-at-home bimbo, wife, and mother: a tethered *Sister X*.

If asked, "What is the difference between the second (2nd) and third (3rd) wave feminist movement?" Margaret would seem interested for a moment. Then, in her eyes, you'd see the "Doe-caught-in-the-headlights" appearance start to creep into Margaret's windows to her soul.

Marge would tear up and say, "This is a stupid question!" But in the back of Margaret's mind, she would consider and contemplate whether the second (2nd) and third (3rd) wave feminist movement was based on skirt height and skirt style from the 1960s? Or maybe the 1970s?

Madeline, her mother, is daydreaming about herself again. Maddy is smoking another cigarette in her Florida room overlooking her forty (40) acre estate with horses, barns, and an apple orchard. She is not looking at the sweeping, beautiful view, but at a reflection of herself in a mirror holding a white wine glass and wearing a two-thousand eight-hundred-dollar ($2,800) dress. Maddy is taking pictures of herself with a selfie-stick pole. Mad strikes poses and makes smoochy faces in the mirror with the two-million-four-hundred-thousand-dollar ($2,400,000) estate as background.

Unfortunately, that visual static interference comes back on my screens. Madeline seems to reminisce about how nice it is to have a successful family here on Mother's Day. But the visual frequencies get crossed on my computer's screens and distort my view. Suddenly there seems to be a veil of false security around Madeline in her Florida room mirror. It is not a natural veil, and so it could not protect her from nature. Her veil is not a moral veil, but the veil made life easier in the Empire State, which is immoral. This immoral veil is a superstitious relic and/or good Psych-Ops — just like the Veil of Veronica. But here in luxurious Allegheny, mother has taken up the Veil of Madeline.

Madeline bellows to her Vietnamese housemaid, "Hoi-Noi! Where's my camera? Pegasus is prancing so beautifully; go take a picture of him and post it on my Facebook (FB) page! And hurry up!"

"Pegasus" is her wild black stallion, her lost sexy-son — her *Object A* - her dreamy, big, black horse she pens-in, bridles, and breaks. Madeline says often and loudly at the Allegheny Country Club, at the wrong time, out of turn, and with crazed eyes, "I keep three (3) or four (4) horses for competitions. The horseys help with my attention-deficit disorder (ADD)."

Madeline, the praying mantis, shakes in an animal-istic ecstasy like the high-strung, drug-addicted white woman she is. It isn't hyper-tension shakes or pre-hyper-tension shakes; it is pre-insanity shakes. Mad is surfing a pre-dementia breakdown — a *Sister X* genetic takedown, that only "The Meds" (Heroin) can control. Madeline is a white, rich woman, not "*En-soi / Pour-soi.*" She is in herself but not for herself.

Madeline is a fashion buyer and merchandiser (FBM) dropout who fancies herself a fashion designer. Madeline McHugh's *haute-couture* (high-fashion) is creative destruction, so Maddy feels safe daydream-ing on pharmaceuticals and a bottle of very fine Chardonnay white wine (approximately one hundred and twenty-three dollars) ($123) in her in Florida room. She is dressed to the nines (9,9,9,9) in a baby-blue satin Fendi gown. She is relaxed and secure - not really safe and secure — but insecure and very expensive. An *En-soi / Pour-soi* woman: not a woman killing it, but an Empire State Florida room with a woman just... in it.

Madeline sees the potential goodness in people, but

only from the point of view of her Florida Room. Like all bulls with blinders who pull a sled for an unknown – known, or an *Other*, she is placed in the barn at night. There is no Virginia Woolf room with a lock and allowances here, only a bull pen / a woman-pen within luxury, filled with her own bullshit. There, within luxury, Madeline paces back and forth questioning / examining *Motherhood* in a doubtful / Socratic way: Mad is an insomniac cow now / a sow now, who used to be a tigress / a mother – just a *frau* now.

Michelle, Madeline's middle daughter and only bio-logical child, enters the Florida room looking more mopey and discontent than usual. Madeline has spent so much time and energy nurturing her two "*Adopted*" daughters that she totally forgot about Michelle, her natural daughter in the middle. What started out as nurturing became de-evolution, and what started out natural became unnatural. The oldest (Margaret) and youngest (Christa) were *Adopted* (human traf-ficking) which... were lot of work compared to the easy flow of blood and nature with Michelle.

The problem with "Adoption" is when it is not *Adoption* but it still is called *Adoption*. Similar to what I explained earlier, how New York Legislature defines, "Corruption and collusion in the Empire is not corruption and collusion." Our politicians say, "It's how we (The Empire) do business." The common sense, *matheme*, or *mathesis* of imperialist *Motherhood* is skewed, drugged, and/or a control-fraud in the Empire State.

That's because when patriarchal *Motherhood*, infer-tility, and the synagogue, mosque, and/or church mix with capitalism, we're back in San Salvadore or Kandahar. We're breeding third-world children to be sold off as soldiers and/or adoptees. Allegheny is dragged back into Iraq or Nicaragua, continuing the same machismo and misogynist power and control over women and her children. This control retards the human soul and is the antithesis of the enlightened English-speaking soul. Regardless, the tables have turned politically, and the colony now becomes the Empire / and the child becomes the mother.

Mothers and children in third-world Rust-Belts are not "En-soi" but "Pour-soi." Mothers and children in third-world Rust-Belts, are not living *In itself*; they are living *For itself*. Mothers and children are not living for themselves; they are living for the Empire. Mothers are not living *"Within Motherhood"*; *they are* living *"For Motherhood."*

When patriarchal *Motherhood* is not questioned, and when that mixes with fertility drugs, child refugees from demilitarized zones (DMZ) and Appalachia, that is when *Adoption* changes from charity to human trafficking and crimes against humanity. *Adoption* or human trafficking of children from Eastern Europe, Asia, impoverished Appalachia, and/or anywhere starvation and poverty exist will seduce a mother to sell her child to the highest bidder. This is human trafficking. This is cannibalism. This is child abuse.

As I wrote earlier, my grandmother in 1906 called it *The Expectant Mother Racket*. What do you call it, Dear Reader? What do I (a lousy mother) working on Mother's Day call it?

After the Supreme Court case of *Roe vs. Wade* (1973), the unwanted and forgotten innocent child — the orphan (the *Other*) — is not *Adopted*, but stolen, and auctioned off as charity. The innocent child, like the soldier, is transferred from base to base to perform their mission. The children, like troops of soldiers, are transferred to perform. This is child abuse.

And genetically created Stem-Cell Sally, who is two (2) months old, is now a lucrative research grant at Harvard University for Deoxyribonucleic Acid

(DNA) manipulation. Stem-cell Sally's friend Stem-Cell Stevey (five (5) months old) is now a genetically modified organism (GMO) in leafy Ivy-League academia. These fascist ministers and scientists are trying to dissect "The *Other*" and "*Nothing*" from our subconsciousness by microscopically dissecting it from our DNA with nanotechnology.

Hollowed-out, divorced children, abused children, the darlings and dolls with issues, and/or the *Adopted* kids, like Cabbage Patch Kids, are the fashionable accessory to have this *Motherhood* season. *Motherhood* with all this "Loving" and "Caring" "For the children" is so the wealthiest families in the Empire can send out Hanukkah and Christmas cards with a family of smiling white faces with even whiter teeth.

During the "Holidays" especially, everyone imagines the *Real* "Family" together... with the brightest blue eyes money can buy. These windows-to-the-soul eyes jump out of Holiday cards wishing everyone a "Happy Holiday and New Year." That's because the card is signed proudly and eloquently NOT by "Mr. Numb Nut and Mrs. Infertility Nut," but it is signed by their five (5) autistic and dyslexic children. All of whom have a matching dead blue eye - approximate cost per child: forty-one thousand ($41,000 X 5 = $205,000 total cost for a "Family" to have "Blue eyes"). The five (5) children sign the card with five (5) "X's" in random parts of the holiday card on the front, middle, and back. I will include this Holiday card as People's Exhibit I because it says way more than a thousand (1,000) words.

Michelle whines, "Howdy, Moommm," in her Appalachian drawl taught to her by the numerous "Local Country" radio stations that are *Intel* mind-control Psych-Ops for the Judeo/Christian tribe in Appalachia.

Confederate flags still fly in the Appalachian

Warm moments...
wishing you these at Christmas

Hallmark

THOMAS KINKADE™
Painter of Light™

Thomas Kinkade, collected artist,
a painter-communicator, infused paintings
bring joy to millions...
Each of his works serves as a quiet reminder of home,
affirming the values of family, health, and
the luminous beauty of nature...
Family Christmas © 2011 Thomas Kinkade

Hallmark Cares
Visit Hallmark.com/ourplanet

THIS CARD IS MADE W...
WELL-MANAGED FOR...

XPX 1761C
© HALLMARK LICENSING, LLC
HALLMARK MARKETING COMPANY, LLC
MADE IN CHINA
Hallmark.com

People's Exhibit I –
Christmas Card Signed By GMO Children

north: religious racism spreads well here, civil wars don't end here, and the Empire Legislature cannot pass humane laws here. Slow, patriotic suicide and disabling xenophobia are the fruits of poverty. The Allegheny Knights of Columbus (K of C), the Kiwanis, and/or the Freemasons are softcore cops dreaming of hardcore inquisitions. These American handlers are linked to the dark pools of power and capital that play the same Psych-Ops *Intelligence* games in Appalachia that we played with the Sunnis in Iraq or the Sandinistas in Nicaragua. The American Empire's handlers are brutal compared to the Knights of Allah (KoA) and the Free Amigos (FA), where *Motherhood* brainwashing was much more compassionate and humane.

Michelle McHugh, Madeline's middle child, has been going to a local Allegheny private college (approximate cost of eighty-two thousand dollars ($82,000) a year) for the last year because she had to drop out of another private college *Downstate* (approximate cost one hundred and twenty-three thousand dollars ($123,000) a year). Michelle dropped out after she overdosed (OD) on white-market pharmaceuticals (legal heroin) in the middle of her presentation in gender studies class.

Michelle had grown up in between two sisters who had been sold to Madeline in a "Private adoption." Both sisters are from poverty in southern Appalachia, but they pretend to be McHughs from Allegheny because it's too painful to play any other role. It's also financially beneficial. The *Adopted* sisters Margaret and Christa, carnally, innately, and biologically vied for control, power, and freedom from their parentless yet enslaved lives. The *Adopted* and/or sold sisters battled like competing animals in a wealthy womb of discontent. The children took the only thing their soulless mothers gave them - their umbilical cord - and they use it to strangle all who get in their way.

Some orphans cling to the adopter mother; other orphans reject it all for the *Other* and/or *Them*. You know those bastards and witches: Steve Jobs, John Lennon, Malcolm X, Henry Ford, Marilyn Monroe, Abraham Lincoln, Edgar Allan Poe, Eleanor Roosevelt, John Hancock, Erasmus, Debbie Harry, Dante, Martin Luther, Jesus Christ, Confucius, and the *numero-uno* bastard of *Them* all: Moses. Dear Family Court and Good Reader, please do not forget Job's iTunes subscription rates ($11.99 a month), "*In Praise of Folly*" by *Erasamus*, and/or Jesus raging in the Bible about society, heredity, and hypocritical Christians not acting like Christians but acting like Country-Club Christians, Luke 14:26:

> If anyone comes to Me and does not hate father and mother, wife and children, brothers and sisters - yes, even their own life - such a person cannot enter my Kingdom.
>
> - Jesus Christ, Luke 14:26

Within the *Mother's Day Madness* "Family," the orphan is the indentured servant whose sole purpose is to play a part, to play a human — a daughter, a son, a disciple? The innocent child is a fashionable social accessory (a human pocketbook? a human fanny-pack?) in order to give power and security to the barren, infertile, and unnatural mothers with low self-esteem. These frantic, hysterical, desperate, and barren spinsters are all victims of the *Expectant Mother Racket.*

The divorced, the abused, the *Adopted* foundling is now "Family" with pedigree. The foundling is on the orphan train going in circles looking for their home called "Ooops," "Ooopsy-ville," "Divorce-ville," or maybe "Mistake-ville."

The train conductor calls out, "Mistake-ville, last stop; last stop, Mistake-ville." But the train doesn't stop or even pretend to slow down at

Mistake-ville. The conductor says, "Ooopsy, guess we're going back again to nature... we'll try again to stop and nurture you up next time around."

The conductor sings out again in a warbled tone, as if this has happened before, and says, "Next stop, *The Real* Child, that's right *The Real* Child is now next, and of course Divorce-ville will be following. Next stop: *The Real Child*, then Divorce-ville, then as usual Nature will be the last stop. Please grab all your metaphysical belongings and emotional baggage. Next stop, *The Real*! This is the Natural Line, last stop — Nature!"

The adopters - the infertile mother and father - seem always to labor more for themselves than for the adoptee. Adopters are part of the problem of child abuse and not part of the solution. No matter what family name is carved onto an orphan's headstone, metaphysically, foundlings will always be buried in an unmarked grave, behind the State Capitol's dumpsters. These lost vagrant souls from orphanages and foundling hospitals are never offered free-grace and bring the play "Nurture vs. Nature" to the vaudeville lights on Broadway, exploiting themselves and grandstanding their tragic and painful lives.

Michelle McHugh, Madeline's middle daughter, leans on the kitchen counter in her favorite outfit, which is Juicy sweatpants ($350) and a H+M T-shirt ($46) and no makeup. Michelle and/or "Mich," as she goes by now, continually looks in the kitchen mirror, playing with her hair. She is walking bowlegged slowly and rubbing her butt like she's injured. Mich's hair is dyed the same Palm Beach bimbo-blond color that Madeline's hair is dyed. Madeline started to dye Michelle's hair when she was six (6) years old once it turned brown after being blond and angelic as a child. Michelle's little *Object A* and her *Real* is the smell and feeling of chlorine bleach burning her hair and scalp. Mich doesn't know her natural hair color, and she doesn't want to know.

Michelle, like all abused children, feverishly gives parental tithes or tariffs to her mother and father in order to maintain her fragile royal family membership: parental Stockholm syndrome (PSS). Mich will never cut the apron string from her mother, and she will become a turned asset for *Motherhood* — a feminine ghost for a man-made invention.

Madeline says, "Good morning, Michelle," in a jubilant yet condescending tone that one would use to calm down a slow child. "How was your party last night?" Madeline needles, wondering if her daughter is still "Dating" the O'Conner boy.

Madeline dreamed of Michelle settling down with Daniel O'Conner as he was sold and/or auctioned with those "*Love*" / breeding-clichés that all proud sponsors of *Motherhood* pitch. Dear Family Court and Good Reader, you know these quips well, as we're all looking with the male gaze and not the female gaze. Women and mothers talk and jabber-jaw about how:

One (1) - "He" is: "A Great Catch,"

Two (2) - "A *Real* Keeper," and/or

Three (3) - "A Handsome Devil."

This language only translates and transforms women into fishermen, salesmen, and devil-dog keepers.

Madeline's lust is social-ladder-climbing; her desires for her daughter to get a hypergamy-whammy was so third-world, misogynist, maligned, and bristling with anti-social psychosis that the fact and knowledge that Michelle was actually drugged and date-raped last night would be redacted and made unimportant in Madeline's mind. She is just like the mothers in Iraq and Afghanistan who proudly hand over their children to perverted military officers as boy-toys. Madeline the thirteen (13) year-old

Baby-Boomer mother, would say, "Well, that's what all the cool kids are doing these days."

In Madeline's teenage mind, she would instead imagine her boastful antics at the Allegheny Country Club where she would gloat and goad the other country club housewives, saying, "My NATURAL daughter is in line to take the royal O'Conner name!" Even though in reality, Dan's frat-boy friends were the only ones being lined up in the dark woods. Lined up in order to turn Danny O'Connor's date-rape of Michelle into a gang-rape of Mich.

Madeline, the saleswoman more than a mother, says to Michelle, "I taped the new "*The Real Housewives of New York (RHNY)*" last night. I can't wait to watch it with you - you'll never guess what happened."

Madeline's statement reminds me of the third letter I hold in my M-8888 satchel. It is a letter to my grandmother from Julia Howe, a great feminist thinker whom my grandmother was working with on her "Mother's Day Proclamation," which was an appeal for mothers to unite to end wars and keep the peace by shaping their societies politically. In this letter from 1870, Julia Howe wrote about how "We will reap what we sow."

> *Dear Madam Anna Jarvis,*
>
> *Thank you for your undying and generous volunteer work with the suffragette clubs in West Virginia and Pennslyvania. Mothers in the future will be eternally grateful to you! They will reap what you have sown!*
>
> *Today I seek your harshest council: please listen with your sharpest ear and tongue. You must read and listen to a new hymn or proclamation I'm working on. I'm writing an appeal to womanhood, and below this brief note is a draft or sketch I'm seeking your opinion on.*

*With my musical words and prose from 1862, I
was able to inspire Union soldiers to end-
lessly kill their Southern neighbors. My
words below are not the "<u>Battle Hymn of
the Republic</u>," but the "<u>Battle Hymn of
Motherhood</u>!" I hope I can inspire mothers on
both sides of any war to enable their children to live rather than to kill. My tortured
soul is at stake!*

*Within our homes, within our prayers, we tend
to our fires; we hold creativity — we hold
the future. This future will have no war
because war is now women's business!*

Sincerely,

Julia Howe

<u>Mother's Day Proclamation</u>

Arise, then... women of this day!

Arise, all women who have hearts,

*Whether your Baptism be that of water or
tears!*

*Say firmly: We will not have great questions
decided by irrelevant agencies.*

*Our husbands shall not come to us, reeking of
carnage, for caresses and applause.*

*Our sons shall not be taken from us to
unlearn.*

*All that we have been able to teach them of
charity, mercy, and patience.*

We, women of one country, will be too ten-
der of those of another country, to allow our
sons to be trained to injure theirs.

From the bosom of the devastated earth a
voice goes up with our own.

It says: Disarm, disarm!

The sword of murder is not the balance of
justice.

Blood does not wipe out dishonor, nor vio-
lence vindicate possession.

As men have forsaken the plough and the anvil
at the summons of war, let women now leave
all that may be left of home for a great
and earnest day of council on this proposed
Mother's Day.

Julia Howe

When I read this letter in 2021, even with the #MeToo movement, all I can think of is my women's book club back in Albany a few months ago. What has *Motherhood* sown and reaped? My women's book club did not discuss the new fourth (4th) wave feminist book, learning how to lean-in together and/or not be abused or harassed. No. Instead, we debated the carnage of "The *Real Housewives of New York (RHNY)*." Our feminine and motherly debate concerned what housewife looked best in her bikini for the wet T-shirt contest.

My book club friend Nancy said, "I like the one with the new fashion line! What is it called? Fatty-Girl? Fat-Ass Girl? Uuum, aaaggh, uumm... now I know! It's called Fatty-Pants! I like Fatty-Pants's ass!"

My other friend Cathy said, "I like Nee-chee's ass!"

Hannah, another book-club girlfriend, rebutted Cathy, saying, "I think Nee-chee is a German philosopher? No, wait... Nee-chee is in Atlanta, Cathy, not New York!"

Including myself, there were six (6) mothers in my Albany Book Club, and we had a total of eighteen (18) children. We were in a four (4) way debate not about *Motherhood* or how to be a better mother to our children, but about Fatty-Pants's fashionlines and bikini contests for Mothers I'd Like to Fuck (MILF). I wondered if these "Women," these "Mothers," understood that their fashionable liberty was their repression and prison. I played along because as a mother, there was nothing else for me to do. I bit my tongue, buried my *Constant Perseverance,* and said, "Pinky's got the best ass!"

Like a psychedelic barber shop quartette in a show tune musical, my book club mothers scaled up and scaled down. They scaled sideways and in and out of harmony. They sang, overlapping each other, reverberating, and echoing, "We *love*, we *love*, we *love*, weee, looovvveeee, we *love* Pinky's, Pinnnkky'ss assssss. Pinky's ass! Pinky's ass, PINKY'S ASS! ASS, ass, AAASSSSSS? They crescendo-ed in dreamy harmony with their chorus, "Aaagghhh, yeah — Pinky's ass!"

I started to sweat and swallow the disgusting fact that me and my motherly friends were not mothers finding a solution to child abuse, but that we / *Us* were the problem.

Cathy said, "I think Nee-chee is gonna hang another one."

She was referring to the *Real Housewives* slang of

divorcing / hanging a man and gouging him for anything and everything he's worth through a divorce.

Hannah said, "You really cannot blame men for the high divorce rate. For the most part, they are the Steady-Eddie Y-chromosome within society."

I think about my own ex, my Steady-Eddie husband whos I divorced. My ex-husband and all the Steady-Eddies out there, if given half a chance, could be the best husband and father a child or mother could want. But these "Housewives" are a man-made creation. I am a man-made creation, with my religionist ideals and my Abrahamic misogyny. My idea of heroine has been perverted into the idea of hero. I'm an Abe-Babe, and our hypergamy-whammy neurosis is, well... the woman. And as the biblical "Woman" advice goes, "No quarrelsome wife, no tears — a life." How can one argue against no cry... a life?

Back to today's investigation and with respect to the Family Court, and as an officer of the *Law* and a veteran of *Intel*, I'm drawn to two incredibly powerful feminine statements from the Julia Howe letter. They have the brutality of triple-tap drone hits at morning funerals for yesterday's dead. The feminine militaristic voice of Julia Howe, unbeknownst to America, is normal chatter at the officers' club over a bourbon or whiskey. Woman in the military are not animals. We are not murderers. We are just trying to survive. The first statement of note:

"Our husbands shall not come to Us, reeking of carnage, for caresses and applause."

How sinister is this statement? How much of this Greek tragedy shall we play as wives, mothers, and arrested heroines? We are mothers with psychological and emotional borders! We are American mothers and women with a history. I understand feminine *caresses* and *applause*, but what is *carnage*?

- 156 -

Is carnage dropping a bomb in a third-world country on a mother or innocent child?

Is destroying your competition unfairly within capitalism carnage? Is firing an employee or mother from their job and destroying their life and family carnage? Is capitalism itself carnage?

Is lying and cheating carnage? Is debt carnage? Is carnage a moral sin or a moral crime?

Who besides the Creator of all humans, Sophia, the Mother and original Creator of the universe, but Julia Howe could burst a "Wounded Warrior's" inflated ego quicker than saying,

> "The sword of murder is not the balance of justice."

or

> "Blood does not wipe out dishonor, nor violence vindicate possession."

And with "Nor violence vindicate possession," Julia Howe seems to suggest especially to a militaristic woman, and to all those that believe "Might Does Make Right," that I / we / *Us* are neutered / infertile... forsaken.... I feel caught, guilty, and exposed as a standing-army control-fraud. Within this lost daydream I wander and exist on a smoldering, lonely, gray battlefield with the dead and half dead. Which am I? Dead? Half-dead? *Us*? *Them*? I don't know....

The *Wounded Warrior* has devolved into the "Wounded Murderer," and all these wandering dead soldiers, sailors, airmen, and marines don't look each other in the eyes. There is no *esprit de corps*. In this strange dream, veterans are ashamed and wander amongst all the heroes and heroines who have killed while they tried to kill-it. Vets are not talking in this strange dream, just bumbling around, heads down amongst the dark, gray clouds. This zombie formalism has movements of pain and agony, but the scene is muted. I'm removed but feel it internally. There is only dread and guilt for eternity with the rest of your "Tribe, Religion, Nation, God, and/ or Friends" who sold their soul for the sword and for the power of might. As a veteran who killed it, will I be left behind after humanity's evolution, after the human ascension?

I'm waking up from this dream feeling infertile and asexual. I feel my face burning from the smack I received from Howe's words and poem. As a child, besides being a slave and having nothing to live for except our *Red-Queen* mother, I was abused, scolded, and grounded for disobeying my mother and Creator, Sophia. Then Big Daddy Reptilian, I AM THAT I AM, would come home from work, pivots, and says, "Might is Right" as he beats Mother Sophia with her broomstick.

I read this feminine poetry, and I can feel moral- ity creeping in. It is the *Other judging* "My game, my gaze" — judging how I chase my *little Object A*. My mother Creator, a poet and prophetess, knows this. On the other hand, I'm being taken away by the Empire because I'm so empty without *the game,* without *the gaze,* without the dream of the *Other* and the *Real*. As a patriarchal mother and child, I slink back to my room incarcerated, without anything to live for — grounded without dinner, grounded with- out my gaze, my game, or my *little Object A*.

Grounded and jailed in my patriarchal room, I'm a mother and child under house arrest. I look around at my patriarchal room, and it changes from free- dom — an artist's white studio — to incarceration and a jail cell. As a mother and child, I stare at the clock. Time is suspended - there are no hands on a Puritan clock, but the "Tick-tock, tick-tock, tick-tock" never stops.

I'm in detention as a bad kid at school, detained like a political prisoner. A woman under patriarchal rule is constantly penalized. She is in the penalty box, not playing on the field, not in the game or even in the race — the human race. She is not a player or even a water-boy / water-girl, but the female is a cheerleader.

As a woman within this human race, I limp along with my child in a three-legged race, hoping for their improvement and education, but the Empire's education is really enforcement and child abuse. As women and mothers, we are not allowed to walk alone in the park thinking about this child abuse. We are not allowed to gather in the park and say, "No more abuse." As mothers, we are not allowed to walk with our children and happiness in the park thinking about *Nothing*....

So, the misogynist Empire ties our legs together in this three-legged race, laughing, and tells *Us*, "It's just a game, it's just a silly race, you're not inferior or handicapped, you're equal to a man. Don't you worry — it's all for the best."

So, as a mother, a child, or a citizen within the Empire, we have of course nothing to live for except the *Real*. *Nothing* is then arrested and held in solitary confinement and called terrorism. *Nothing* is a wildflower drug that can steer a wild man or an immature man insane, but *Nothing* also makes a gentleman out of the wild man. *Nothing* makes a wild woman a lady, but the *Real* has nothing to do with *Nothing*.

Chapter 13

10:18 A.M. - <u>MOTHER FALLS AND IS HELPED</u> <u>BY BILLY SIMON</u>, OR, COMPLAINT #21-4532

I've pulled up to my stakeout position for Complaint #21-4532 and can see via my screens and cell phone data logs that Barbara Dalton has just gotten off the phone with her oldest daughter. Barbara seems to be getting anxious and irritated in her basement crawl space. She paces and mutters to herself in her ashtray crawl space. That's because now is when her drunk husband and daughter would be getting up to start drinking again. Barbara has *little Object As* and *big Objects As* in her house. There are also *Other* objects: her grandchildren.

Diana and Craig usually get on the school bus around 7:45 a.m. Barbara counts on a little respite from the bloodbath of her life between 7:45 a.m. and 9:45 a.m. Here on Mother's Day, a Sunday, the kids and the adults are all sleeping in, so her family recess in her smoky crawl space continues uninterrupted.

Left alone in her earthen room, Barbara smokes her spliff slowly. She seems to wonder whether her jan- itorial job is going to last another two and a half (2 ½) years till her retirement. The Seneca Council

members' tribe has many "Internal tribes" that constantly fight for the "True" Seneca "Turtle-power."
Barbara only understands Indian politics from it
being broadcast by her coworkers. Skinny Larry, who
weighs about three hundred and fifty (350) pounds,
and fat Bobby, who weighs about one hundred and
twenty-five (125) pounds, are always fighting each
other for everyone's entertainment in their whitey
basement breakroom. The broadcast from the asbestos
man-cave provides a daily update that is bookended
with either a smoke break and/or snoozing during a
group nap.

Via the Seneca Nation's security system, I watched
the maintenance engineers' man cave from earlier
this morning. It was about the hour of the wolf
around three-thirty Ante Meridiem (3:30 a.m.),
and the Appalachian Southern drawls and evangel-
ical singsongs competed for attention. Larry from
Livermore was spinning the rumor that "The Seneca
Turtle people are going to buy out the Bear people,
and all the white people are going to be fired."

Barbara and her peers all chewed and licked their
GMO dinners from the vending machine as Skinny
Larry stood on a plastic chair, causing it to bend
and contort under his massive weight. The food
wrappers crinkled so much that it sounded like
mice quickly building an indoor November home after
the temperature dives into the freezing teens. The
scurrying and crinkling mixed well with the sound
of sliding silver coins into the vending machines.
These impoverished folks, these humans living in
America's third-word feed themselves, nourished
themselves from rat-food machines — it is fright-
ening and hard to watch.

The long silver pulley and/or button grants you
your nutritional choice. "A5... no, shit... okay,
L2... Oops, wrong button... P5... no, okay, what-
ever...." The game is called "Nutrition," and you
never get what your body wants – positive energy.

People's Exhibit J –
Vending Machine Nutrition

The breakroom sounded like an arcade or game room. Red, white, and blue chewy chocolate wrappers and lime-colored Mountain Dew bottles littered the dirty white tile floor. Forever chemicals (PFA) and bile-yellow corn syrup were being grinded by teeth and absorbed into brain tissue as flashing pachinko lights slapped steel pinballs into glass plates and rubber bumpers.

Skinny Larry exclaimed, "We need to form a union and organize!" Other employees within this rat lab test waved their hands and feet, exclaiming, "Aaaammmmeeeennnnn."

Fat Bobby jumped up on the break room table and tried to slow everyone down. He pleaded slowly, "Y'all is crazy, just plum-fucking crazy." As he looked everyone in the eye and repeated, "Y'all is really fucking crazy."

Billy Simon, a scrawny, ashen man who stood hunched over, was the shape of a sickle. Billy had dark hair and eyes the color of black coal, and he was rumored to be part Seneca (the Wolf Clan). Billy jumped up on a corner table and exclaimed, "What is our employer doing for *Us*? They're killing *Us*!!! Are we doing better than our Baby-Boomer parents? NO, our Me-Generation parents sold *Us* - their children - to the Seneca for eternal youth! We are ALL CURSED to get never ahead in life. So now our food, our clothing, and our shelters are cursed for eternity!"

Billy put his hands over his face and twitched and wiggled in pain on the table as we all watched....

Someone said, "Injuns didn't shut down the Furniture Factory."

Another person spoke up and declared very clearly, "Clinton and the Democrats shut down the factory. The North American Free Trade Act did. NAFTA did!"

The bluish florescent lights flickered as this serious thought was added to the break-room conversation. A sad hush fell over the room as white, blue, and purplish strobe lights pulsated onto the stunned fat white faces of the whitey breakroom. They collectively thought, *"Has the Empire fucked Us? Maybe it's not just the Indians fucking Us?"*

This questioning was the whitey tilt — game over for whitey cracker. The pinball machine, like Plato's Payola, sang a snarky downbeat song ending with your demise, your money gone, your tools frozen, and the lights turned out. These thoughts floated around the breakroom within dark quietude while the strobing and crackling fluorescent light above *Them* sputtered and sizzled back to its luminous white / blue glow hum.

Bobby Simon stood up on his toes, still on his corner table. He was energized by the blue light and said, "We have fallen, we have to admit defeat, but we need to unionize now against the Seneca."

Another worker brought it back to the *Real*, "But we need to feed our family!"

Hearing this, Barbara Dalton's heart seemed to fall as she nodded her head in agreement about feeding her family and exclaimed very quietly with others, "Amen, Amen, Amen."

Her husband, her daughter, and her grandchildren sucked her weekly paycheck of two hundred and fifteen ($215) dollars from her before she could deposit it. Barbara is working forty (40) hours a week, has no savings, and has lived paycheck to paycheck. Barbara is also on food stamps at sixty-two (62) years old, in need as a mother to her delinquent daughter's two (2) children.

Simon said, "If we don't unionize, they will crucify *Us* to their Injun cross like they did during the American Revolution and the War of 1812. The British hired the Seneca as mercenaries, as rats to kill *Us*. And now the Seneca will hire illegals to work as mercenaries - as rats to try and kill *Us* again."

There was complete silence again in the breakroom, and the light-blue, fluorescent light flickered again - a new depth of desperation took over their cobalt faces. That was because everyone already knew the Seneca were already hiring illegal Latinos. Simon knew this but was playing to his audience's common denominator of stupidity.

Within this silence brought on by Simon, the asbestos paint peeled off the break room's ceiling and walls. Bedpan colors - like pastel pinks, light blues, and lime greens - curled, showing the color palette of insane asylums from the 1950s to 1970s. Psychological and analytical institutional colors mixed well with padded rooms, electroshock therapy, and Lysergic Acid Diethylamide (LSD) experiments. Lobotomy-lime walls encircled the operating rooms as playful pinks and baby blues dressed up the waiting room and entrance. These colors and the dialogue made me think I was watching more rat lab tests.

Simon asked, "Where will you move when the Indian and the Empire foreclose on you?

Barbara Dalton and her peers owned their houses in Allegheny, but their houses sat on Seneca Indian land, so they didn't own their houses - whitey rented on the Rez. The Seneca Indians had obviously had English lawyers from King's Road, London, negotiating their land Contracts for *Them* back in 1784 and 1815 after the American patriots beat *Them* back twice. Accordingly, the Seneca were now so rich from their cigarette and gambling casino profits that they were buying up Allegheny property.

Someone in the back of the breakroom said, "The Seneca's tax liens are too expensive – my family and I are being foreclosed on...."

The breakroom returned to silence once again. Barbara and the Daltons (as most people in the breakroom) were about two (2) years behind on their rent / taxes due to the Seneca Indians. The Seneca Indians were foreclosing on these properties with their gambling casino and cigarette cash. The native Seneca were bulldozing whitey Appalachian houses into dust and then joyfully watching as these fields slowly turned into colorful fields of wildflowers.

The Seneca were now orchestrating a reversal of American Manifest Destiny and have turned Allegheny life into Seneca Turtle Destiny. The Indian Removal Act of 1830 has been replaced with the White Trash Removal Act of 2021.

Chapter 14

12:08 A.M. — MOTHER PROMISES HER KINGDOM TO AN UNREPENTANT THIEF — HER DOG, OR, COMPLAINT #21-6154

It's just after midnight, and I've returned to the Highland Avenue stakeout location for Complaint #21-6154. I'm looking at my three (3) laptops and I see Madeline in her kitchen playing with one (1) of her six (6) *Adopted* and/or rescued lap dogs. Madeline's motherly *love* for her lapdogs does not come cheap at the average cost of eight thousand eight hundred dollars ($8,800) per dog annually. For six (6) dogs, Mad spends almost fifty-four thousand ($54,000) dollars per year to "Care" for them. There are the doggy sweaters for the winter, the lactose-free organic doggy food, the doggy summer camps, the holiday outfits, and their weekly doggy-doo bath and shampoo. Madeline's husband categorizes her "Pet expenses" as a home / office expense and deducts approximately sixty-four thousand dollars ($64,000) from his average annual income of roughly two million dollars ($2,000,000).

The McHugh dogs include: Gucci, Hershey, Louis, Chanel, Ralphy, and Lauren in tribute to Maddy's true calling in life: eating chocolate bonbons while shopping online for expensive crap to fill up the empty *Real*. The annual doggy health care for this luxurious household could feed a third-world family of four (4) in Central America, the Middle East, or in West Virginia Appalachia for approximately six (6) years.

Madeline now feeds the six (6) doggies at her feet opium (heroin) laced doggy treats as they all dance around in circles in her fifteen-hundred (1,500) square-foot kitchen. Maddy and her doggies look small and ridiculous in this big McMansion kitchen that is the same size kitchen as a medium-size prison or soup kitchen for the homeless.

Madeline says to her doggies, "You shall inherit this kingdom — my only true *lovers*!" as she dances around in junkie doggy circles spraying "Smacky-Smack, Ding-Dong, Doggy Snacks" like a water sprinkler to six (6) dancing dogs high on black tar.

Madeline, like most American women, thinks her life's calling is to be, or should be, "A mother." Somewhere between *Mary* and *Eve*, there is the signifier "Mother" - a little object, a little death, a *jouissance*. Madeline the mother and her little object is engendered by her conqueror. Therefore, Madeline cannot handle a relationship with herself, much less with a child or, more importantly, with a member of the opposite sex.

Madeline exclaims, "Gucci, you are the only heir in my will, Gucci-baby, you are the only blood in my heart." Gucci, the unrepentant thief, distracts Madeline by giving her licky-lick kisses on Madeline's face so Gucci's buddies (Chanel and Ralphy) can ransack the "Smacky-Smack, Ding-Dong, Doggy Snack" closet that has approximately three thousand one hundred and fifty-three dollars ($3,153) worth of dog food.

But the Rolling Stones forewarned *Us* of the American woman tragedy in 1966 with their song <u>"Mother's</u>

<u>Little Helper</u>." Those musical dandies start the song with their sloppy, out-of-tune sitar hook introduction, and they then saunter along and sing like doomed drunken sailors in a rudderless ship called "<u>Opium Den</u>" on its way to the Opium Wars (1860). The song satirically lambastes the American housewife. You know the song that opens with a strange introduction about how horrible it is to age badly? With no music, a male vocalist sings / taunts, "What a drag it is getting old."

There is a nice pause, and the trippy sitar slowly starts to worm its way up to a good volume before the lyrics start. The vocalist continues to taunt by conjuring mothers complaining about their kids being big pains in the ass. The lyricist illuminates why, because of the stress of raising children, so many 1960s mothers secretly depended on pharmaceuticals to simply endure their existence and/or appear normal.

The Opium Wars in 1830 and 1860 happened when the British East India Company (EIC) tried to monopolize the alien poppy plant that Sumerian Gods brought from their planet Nibiru. You know Nibiru - out there in the Zeta Reticuli galaxy. You know Nibiru, around the corner from Planet X and right next door to Planet Nine (9). It's supposedly a nice, gated community, Zeta Reticuli, although I hear the Cooperative (Co-op) Board for purchase approval is a nightmare.

Regardless, during the two (2) Opium Wars, the great-grandfathers of the Rolling Stones and their ilk sat on British battleships trying to corner the market and monopolize the poppy plant in both India and China. The East India Trading Company won both wars and then essentially sold the opium trade to Purdue Pharma in 1892. Who then sold it to the Sackler family in 1952.

But I still don't know why any levelheaded human

would venture within ten feet (10 ft.) of any of the Sackler family's creative destructive pills, OxyContin or Sublimaze. That's because they have never seen the very alive poppy plant slithering around in action like the alien snake it is.

My Air Force *Intel* Unit was in the high desert of Iran near the Pakistan border back in the mid-1980s. The area was mostly dry with sporadic scrub brush. But where there was water - there was *Intel*, and where there was *Intel* - there were also poppy fields. Therefore, my Unit was dressed as nomadic opium harvest workers. We were coming down a small mountain range on one of those stunning Middle East mornings that are clear and bright. The cobalt blue of the sky was so blue, and the cotton white of the clouds was so white you could taste and hear these colors.

The Middle East atmosphere has this strange stratosphere that is similar to living on the clear and bright East Coast of America. The east coast has reflective water all around, and this refractory light bounces off the water, and then the clouds create a supersonic white all day and then a pink glow at sunset. The lights from the sun to the water to the clouds circle in continuous illumination, but here in landlocked Iran, that same radiance is in these mysterious mountains.

As we approached the valley floor, we could see the pink and white flowers blanketed and stretched out for about fifteen (15) to twenty (20) acres. The poppy flowers had feathery petals that flitted about like flames four (4) feet off the ground. Amongst these feathery flowers were the scarified poppy seed pods that stood a commanding eight (8) to ten (10) feet. The pods were all facing the warm yellow sun and seemed to be having a beach party, laughing, hooping, and hollering. As we got closer to the poppy fields, the other crews looked over nervously at us, so our Iranian *Intel* guides went over to see if we could be hired. The rest of our

Intel team stood around smoking cigarettes in order to assimilate as normal nomads.

But the poppy pods all suddenly halted their beach-bingo party and stopped facing the sun. The alien poppy pod snakes all started to slowly turn towards my *Intel* team. The poppy pod snakes moved in unison like Cobra line dancers extending themselves high, and then they swooped in low. Then these green snakes wiggled left and right into a firm position like a crouching tiger or a wrestler about to grapple.

The opium harvest workers picked up this change in the Middle Eastern stratosphere immediately and started to gather and walk quickly to the opium harvesting boss. He was in a dusty four-wheel-drive (4WD) Toyota pickup truck with a large automatic weapon crudely mounted on the top of his front cab.

At the same time, the poppy plants started to slowly, one by one, turn and face *Us*. The poppy plants were sizing-up my *Intel* team and ready to rumble. The poppy plant narcotics were narcing on *Us* to the Iranians! My *Intel* peers, and some very experienced *Intelligence* commandos, started to shit themselves. Rightfully so because within a moment, we watched in horror as both of our Iranian *Intel* guides started pointing towards *Us* and yelling some nasty anti-American crap. Our *Intel* guides were doing the "Rat" dance, and we were super-fucked way behind enemy lines.

The opium boss and his team quickly got into offense mode and shot the Iranian *Intel* guides in the back of their heads as they were yelling and pointing at *Us*. My team quickly morphed into survival, evasion, and rescue mode that lasted three (3) revolting days and nights on the run in the mountains of Iran. After getting pinned down for the fourth (4th) time and losing numerous members of the team, our

Officer in Charge (OC) had to call-in for help...
and asking for help is failure for *Intel*.

Combat Controllers (CCT) and Pararescue (PJ)
Specialists had to perform a High Altitude - Low
Opening (HALO) insertion with an HH-60 Pave Hawk
helicopter extraction in order to get *Us* / a covert
Intel team out.

Honorable Family Court and Good Reader, I digress,
and I want to move-on, but let me state here and
now: those Poppy snakes are aliens with psychic
powers, and the opium blood that our children and
society are addicted to - is not from this earth.

Going back to the Rolling Stones in 1966 who were
laughing at American women just like those poppy
snakes. Today, on May 9th, 2021, let's step back
even further in time to when the "Innocent Child"
was the new sucker, the new pansy, the new mark
for a *Mother's Little Helper* and/or "Smacky-Smack,
Ding-Dong, Doggy Snacks."

So, let's give it up, Family Court, Good Reader,
and now Good Listener, for the new American Country
band, **The Sumerian Stones** and their new 2021 hit,
titled:

"Innocent Child's Little Helper."

"Mothers are different today,"
I hear all the Innocent Children say;
Innocent Child needs something to calm down.
And though they're not really ill,
there's a little Opioid pill.

They go running for the shelter of their
Innocent Child's Little Helper.

Doctor, please, some more of those.
Outside the door, they took four more.

What a drag it is being young.
Life's just much too hard today, I hear every
Innocent Little Child say.

The pursuit of happiness just seems a bore.

And if you take more of those, you'll overdose.
No more running for the shelter of an Innocent
Child's Little Helper.

When the enemy of our American Revolution for Life, Liberty, and the Pursuit of Happiness sings to you that your women are pathetic, you know you've already lost. The American woman had become a national security risk in 1966.

That's because in military science, your enemies are more revealing / helpful than your allies. Meaning that your friends are useless, but your ene-mies will keep you sharp. But many American women, instead of wising-up like smart female owls, seem to be descending further into child-abuse called American *Motherhood*.

Unfortunately, after my own divorce from a dead-beat Yankee husband, I stopped lying to myself. So therefore, I'm not "Motherly," nor do I try to be. I'm *Mama-Non-Grata*. My husband and our mar-riage were so miserable that I must confess that I had my children just because I didn't want to deal with "Him" anymore. My husband was a good-natured man, but I emasculated him / sent him away like a seasonal laborer or a migrant worker after he plowed and planted his seeds. I, or maybe women in general, should not be surprised when the patriar-chal *Red-Queen* marriage without money doesn't work. Please, women and mothers: you know whose fault it was – and whose fault it is.

I, like Madeline McHugh, capitalized and imperial-ized my husband and our children's lives with veils and vines / with smoke and mirrors. The difference is that my ex-husband could NOT afford ($$$) my patriarchal magic show. But Madeline's white-devil husband not only paved the way and pruned the trees for every walk Madeline took, he paid legal and illegal immigrants to carry her the whole time. Mr. McHugh paid through the nose for each of his three (3) descendants (the average cost of each daughter raised in their tax bracket is nine hundred and fifty thousand dollars ($950,000)). It takes about a million ($1,000,000) for a woman to have a well-educated child. That's all-private education through a graduate degree, law, or medical degree. The three million ($3,000,000) needed for Madeline's children is a drop in the bottomless and endless Dead Sea called "Ego," "Heredity," and/or "Royalty."

Our motherly *love* is an ivy vine — it is a veil. Man is hollowed out and curtained off like that of a green, vine-covered tree. The tree looks healthy, lush, and leafy from afar in the green seasons as the watery, fragile female green vines are spreading over the very male dead skeleton of the old tree / of the old man. Even in the cold and dark winter, a hollow and dead husband looks green and alive with an ivy woman wrapped around him.

The feminine, cold truth underneath our green and natural blanket – as it suffocates our husband – is that our veil of womanhood: our anarchy, our adultery, and our artistry – kills the tree. Good growth is forsaken, taken over by an overbearing female weed, a *Red-Queen Ivy*, and/or a flighty vine because of too much ego, hierarchy, and/or patriarchy.

In contrast, the empirical poison ivy within the Ivy League is not feminine. It's masculine, incarcerating, and was created to suppress women. John Winthrop and John Harvard created the poison Ivy at Harvard College in 1636 to specifically suppress Anne Hutchinson and the Free-Grace philosophy. This Ivy League school and all her un-American royal offspring (Yale, Dartmouth, Columbia, Penn State, Brown, Princeton, and Cornell) are party to this female suppression of free-speech, equality, and Free-Grace to this very day.

And if you don't believe me, Family Court and Good Reader, please check-out a great book that explains this anti-feminist Ivy League mission. The eloquent book is entitled, "The Worming of America, Or, An Answer to the Arraignment of Women," 2018 by Autumn Leaf.

The book is a diary from 1650 Boston, written by the daughter of Anne Hutchinson - Susan Hutchinson. But Susan wrote her diary in her Lenape Indian name - Autumn Leaf. Susan was taken hostage in 1645 by those Lenape natives and renamed Autumn Leaf because of her red hair. Autumn Leaf explains everything you need to know about the foundation of America during its formation in 1650 Boston. Autumn explains how John Winthrop and John Harvard created Harvard to suppress women and Free-Grace. Harvard and the Ivy League are an education system where only royalist-loyalists survive.

The book also correctly places the first act of "Civil Disobedience" in America with Mary Dyer in 1650. It wasn't Henry Thoreau in 1849 that Martin Luther King (MLK) and Mahatma Gandi were inspired by. It was Mary Dyer, who left Shelter Island, New York on a sunny spring day and went north to Boston to be hanged by the royalist-loyalists John Harvard and his Ivy League.

I can see on my screen: Madeline is in her garden, with white children running about, with a white-devil McMansion in the background, all behind a white-picket fence, with full-time white security, guards in a white zip code, within a white Empire.

Madeline is trying to raise the new Emperor and/or Empress of the Empire with strings attached. Mother and the Empire need a kickback, and if she doesn't get it — hell hath no fury.

The problem with Madeline's garden is that it is dug and tended by Jose her Guatemalan landscaper, picked over by Hoi-Noi, her Vietnamese housekeeper, and secured by "Bob," a child molester from eastern Europe using an alias and posing as a nighttime security officer. Madeline does not tend her garden; she bought - excuse me - her husband bought her garden for her. Madeline does enjoy and encourage her six dogs to defecate in her garden. It is because she read an article in "Vogue" about the benefits of excrement — much to the chagrin of Jose, the gardener.

Hoi-Noi the housekeeper does try to find fruit or vegetables in Madeline's garden, but the infestation of beetles, mites, and varmint makes Hoi-Noi's search futile. Hoi-Noi instead goes to the local Waldbaum's food market and buys large healthy tomatoes, cucumbers, and carrots from the produce section and places *Them* in Madeline's "Garden basket" during harvest season.

Madeline is so easily excited by the slightest indication that proves she is materially alive. So, this faux garden triumph for Madeline is just as fabulous as a birthday party invitation from a thirteen (13) year-old bimbo "Cool girl." Every day is a birthday party for Madeline; the problem is that no one shows up for Madeline's parties unless they are paid... extremely well.

Upon seeing the "Freshly picked fruits and vegetables from the garden," Madeline holds her fruits and vegetables to the sky and thanks Jesus for these gifts of life. She kisses and hugs these inanimate objects the way a child protects her doll. Madeline proudly coddles and fawns over her fruits and vegetables (just as she does with her children). Madeline poses for Hoi-Noi, ordering her to take pictures of her with her fruit and vegetable children so she can post on Facebook (FB) and out-mother her motherly competition.

Sadly, as Madeline is giving thanks to her Lord Cucumber, Hoi-Noi realizes that she left the Waldbaum's price tags on the tomatoes Madeline is holding up to the Judeo-Christian miracle sky. Hoi-Noi doesn't know what to do.... Madeline closes her eyes and starts mumbling one of her Catholic fairy-tale prayers. Hoi-Noi starts panicking and freaking, as she is a recently converted Catholic.

Hoi-Noi was told four (4) years ago by her Buddhist Elder (her *Real* faith) that "The Catholic thing" would help her housekeeping business. On her Federal and State taxes, Hoi-Noi's income has quadrupled (4X) in the last three (3) years.

Hoi-Noi reaches up to the tomatoes, covering the Waldbaum's price tags Madeline blindly holds above her head, and starts mumbling along with Madeline in psychotic prayer.

Madeline, suddenly, out of the blue, stops her rosary recital mid-prayer. With eyes wide open and excited at this shared religious revelation, Maddy says in a hushed way to Hoi-Noi, "I knew you little Commies would make great Catholics!"

Hoi-Noi joins Madeline in her deep delusionary delirium heaven. An Empire State Catholic prayer thanking their Lord Savior – Saint Waldbaum – for coming back from the dead, being born from a virgin, and delivering these exceptional fruits and vegetables ($87) to their garden!

St. Waldbaum, living for the garden instead of living for himself, reminds me of the fourth (4th) letter I hold in my M-8888 folder. It is from my Great-Grandmother Catherine Reeves, explaining

People's Exhibit K —
The Fruit of Madeline's Garden

Margaret Fuller to my Grandmother Anna Jarvis. In
the letter, Catherine Reeves explains gardening
in a sense and Margaret Fuller's heavy text in
"The Great Lawsuit, Men Versus Man, Women Versus
Woman," 1845. My Great-Grandmother Catherine
wrote:

> *To My Loveliest Daughter, Anna,*
>
> *Can you believe your father is not back from
> his California trip? I'm starting to worry,
> but I know your father will show up soon.*
>
> *I just finished the new Margaret Fuller book.
> It's an expansion of her writing at the lit-
> erary journal "The Dial," which I've sent you
> before. "Women in the Nineteenth Century" is a
> little too out there for me. Besides, she and
> those New England folks always seem so sen-
> timental — so self-righteous. Always talking
> about nature as if it is some God and that
> we are here "To tend some garden or plough
> the earth"? I don't get it... her voice, her
> tone, is too preachy. The thesis is about the
> self-reliant and independent woman. It's very
> Ralph Waldo Emerson; it's all very academic
> and manly!*
>
> *I did like a lot of her writing about tran-
> scendentalism. The title, "The Great Lawsuit"
> as "The Great Sin" or "The Great Swindle,"
> really speaks to the gravitas of her vision.
> It also speaks to her sarcastic and sappy
> form! Does she write for herself or to all
> women? She sounds like a woman lawyer — what
> a frightening thought!*
>
> *Is she 'En-soi' or 'Pour-soi?' Is she being
> in-itself or being for-itself - I don't
> know.... Is Margaret Fuller exploring her-
> self and sharing for the world to see in good
> faith, or is she a woman litigating in bad*

*faith against the Other? I cannot judge; I
will not judge!*

*I will send you the book, and you don't have
to return it.*

*Love, Always... and Remember Life Is Not a
Bowl of Cherries, Your Mother,*

Catherine Reeves

This letter was stuck in the back of the Margaret
Fuller book "*Women in the Nineteenth Century*."
My Grandmother Anna Jarvis would read this book
to herself but couldn't or wouldn't understand
Fuller's purpose. Fuller and transcendentalism
wasn't passed on to me during my grandmother's
life. I did not find this letter or her copy of
Fuller's book till after my grandmother died.
Despite this motherly censorship, I've read
Margaret Fuller's work my whole life. In fact,
over and over, many times. Not for revenge, but
for balance. My Tough Nurse Grandma Jarvis was
also my Prude Grandmother Jarvis. She scribbled
notes of disapproval and disgust around Margaret
Fuller's chapters on sexual relationships. I *love*
and respect my Grandmother Anna Jarvis for eternity, but her sexual dishonor in 1938 hurts femininity to this day in 2021.

Fuller was a nineteenth (19th) century fox, but two
hundred (200) years before her time, and I channel her up frequently on Thursday nights with my
Rosicrucian friends. My Grandma Anna, is always
there also. She incarnates frequently and tells me
secrets.

But Mary Fuller and I walk and talk to each other
along the seashore of Fire Island on Long Island, New
York, where she drowned in 1850. We walk along the
beach break and search for seashells and nice-look-
ing rocks... We look at the beautiful and balanced

seashell's golden-ratio construction and aesthet-
ics. We talk about Sophia as Creator. Sometimes,
Mary just listens even when I don't speak a word.

Chapter 15

It's early afternoon, and I'm staked-out on Dam
Road. My mics and exterior cams are clear and target
#21-4532, Barbara Dalton, as she enjoys her Mother's
Day doing the dishes while her husband and daughter get stoned on the back porch. Neither of *Them*
have wished Barbara a happy Mother's Day yet. The
gray-green sun in Allegheny suddenly splinters, and
a sunbeam breaks-out for a few moments and shines,
illuminates, and cleans their broken-down porch that
is ten (10) feet by twelve (12) feet. The porch is
more of a raft than a porch. The Dalton porch is
more like "*The Raft of Medusa*" (1819), a painting by
Gericault that depicts a catastrophe in which a raft
of sailors are cannibalizing each other after their
ship was wrecked and they float around aimlessly.
So therefore, here in 2021 Appalachia, everyone's
porch is not called "The Raft of Medusa," but "The
Raft of Poverty."

And Honorable Family Court and Good Reader, I don't
know if you like to look at fine-art paintings,
drawings, or illustrations because then you would
be an aesthetician and/or "A Good Looker." But my

watercolor painting, which I will share with this Court will show a sad composition of mothers cannibalizing their families and children with abstract trash. My watercolor painting "The Raft of Poverty" is "People's Exhibit L."

The Appalachian front porch and/or their "Raft of Poverty" first and foremost has used tires hiding underneath the porch raft and in the corners, to keep it afloat. Then beer can recyclables ($0.05) are littered and strewn across the raft / porch in loosely tied clear bags that have thousands (1,000s) of beer cans. The next great architectural feat on the "Raft of Poverty" is the children's colorful plastic fort with slides that was used once or twice by their insolent and discontent children and then forgotten forever. The forts / slides quickly fade in the sun's ultraviolet (UV) rays and become yet another vessel to carry more unrecycled beer cans that will never be recycled ($0.05).

The third big improvement for the Appalachian "Raft of Poverty" in 2021 is the kiddie pool filled with green putrid water and more beer cans. From the mast of this "Raft of Poverty" swings an old car seat crudely hung with big chains as some kind of swinging Appalachian loveseat. On the sides of these rafts are always dilapidated cars and trucks on blocks. Because Barbara's husband was an old rock star of Allegheny, she has two (2) 1976 Pontiac Trans Am hotrods on blocks. One (1) Trans Am is smashed into a washer / dryer set on the porch / raft, and the other was buried under more used tires and beer can recyclables. Barbara, the mother of the house, has magically planted yellow-and-black black-eyed Susans all around and in the old Trans Ams car. She perfectly matched the black-and-gold Trans Am with its famous "Smokey and the Bandit" color scheme.

This dreary black-and-white watercolor painting of spiritual cannibals on "The Raft of Poverty" is particularly horrifying because no humans are there except their trash - their leavings... their compost. Because Appalachia is so vacant and xenophobic, no one is looking to be "Saved." No cannibal is looking for another ship on the horizon, poverty does not ask for help, poverty dies alone on its own Dead Sea amongst the trash, which outlives poverty by many decades.

Susan and Bill, now stoned / disengaged, sit in a slouched and dejected manner on their small wooden raft. They look like two large naked blobs of mozzarella cheese on a small dirty cracker. It is forty-eight (48) degrees, and the sun has popped out for fifteen (15) minutes or so here on Dam Road. Here in northern Appalachia, any temperature above forty-five (45) degrees marks the beginning of summer, so all the Allegheny rednecks are out sunbathing, including Susan and Bill. They are racing, as usual, to see who will pass out or fall first. An alcoholic or addict's life slipping from the morning nip, to the afternoon liquid-lunch, to a happy hour buffet, and then a little nightcap to keep the "Shakes" away. Then... subconscious again, slipping and sleeping into bedtime, early time, sleepy time, no dreamtime — alcoholic and addict time. I know this time.

Both targets are on their fourth (4th) or fifth (5th) beer, as Barbara had just made a "Rez" run to get more tax-free cigarettes and beers.

Barbara's grandchildren are out biking with the neighbor kids across the street when they suddenly come screeching in on their little motocross (BMX) bikes. "Happy Mother's Day," they scream in Appalachian redneck harmony, which is not exactly audible unless you have a good ear and a sixth (6th) sense. Bill and Susan look at each other, startled by this vocal outburst. Their sea of green (SoG) joint they are smoking is nothing more than a roach

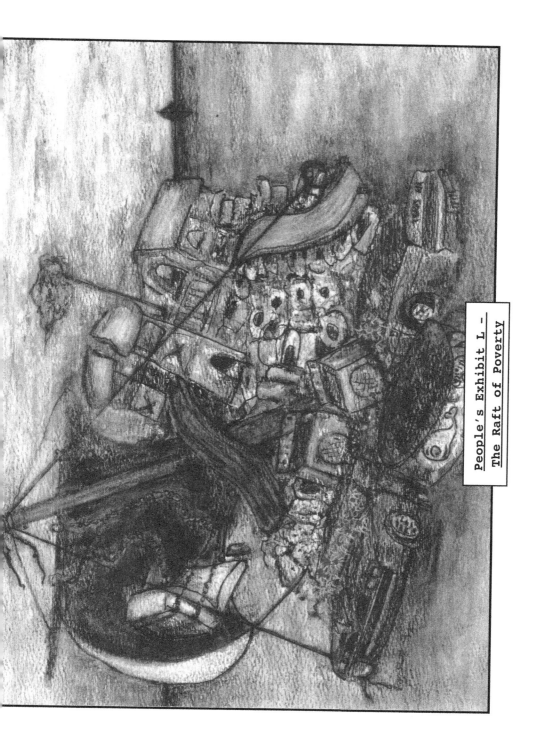

People's Exhibit L –
The Raft of Poverty

at this point. They are both uncomfortably numb and deep in Dalton discontent.

From a foggy haze, they grunt and growl into slow and separate escalating and echoing choruses, "Shut, shut, shut, shut, shut, shut, shut... The, the, the, the, the, the, the... Fuck, fuck, fuck, fuck, fuck, fuck, fuck... Up, up, up, up, up, up, up...."

Diana and Craig answer the parental duet with, "Happy Mother's Day!" And now it has a resounding retort on a wider frequency scale, more resilient, and with a vibrato.

The dueling duet turns bombastic with Mahler thunder as the grandfather, Bill Dalton, and daughter, Susan Dalton, set the Appalachian bar with, "Shut the fuck-up," drawn out in a Southern, totalitarian tone. "Shuuuut the fuuuuccccccck uuuuuup!"

Diana and Craig encircle and chase each other within the Daltons' muddy driveway on their BMX bikes. Muddy whoops, hollers, and screams of dangerous child's play ring out shrilly. Next to the driveway is the small porch where the flabby Dalton walruses sun themselves on their death raft. All of a sudden, the sun disappears - there is no sun now. The gray leaden clouds of inland America have rolled back in, blocking out the sun again. Diana and Craig weave in and out, going round and round in BMX merry-go-round merriment. Bill and Susan get spooked by the escalating buzz of their children's bicycle tires going faster and faster through muddy, watery puddles. The children's buzz is slowly intensifying as their wheels come closer and closer to the floating walruses on the Daltons' "_Raft of Poverty_."

Besides the deep red pothole puddles, the driveway has high desert plateaus, and a dust storm starts to rise as Diana and Craig, in a menacing key, start humming, taunting, and chanting, "Happy Mother's Day, Happy Mother's Day, Happy Mother's Day."

Bill, the children's grandfather, exclaims to Susan, "Great... Look, the Hari Krishna are here. What are your children even mumbling?"

Diana and Craig's hypnotic hot yoga breath mantra of, "Happy Mother's Day, Happy Mother's Day, Happy Mother's Day," comes in on an intelligent dance music (IDM) sine wave blipping, blopping, and glitching from a black hole or third eye. Diana and Craig dance with gentle, floating, square waves, brain-dancing. The children are busy wind chimes dinging and donging in a stiff breeze; the children are clinking and clanking in harmony from another galaxy. They were desperately trying to communicate to *Us* with musical sound waves and frequencies that we pretend we don't understand or cannot hear.

Diana and Craig run with their sketchy beats, singing: "Happy Mother's Day, Happy Mother's Day, Happy Mother's Day!" And in between their taunts, their silence is a scary space — the deepest beat. This deep space in between beats is a breakbeat, in between life and death. This glitchy breakbeat lives in between heartbeats.

Susan and Bill, Allegheny's redneck elite – because they shit, piss, and disrespect everything kill the stagnant silence of the Southern Tier by yelling again, "Shut... the... fuck... up!"

Diana and Craig's BMX bikes with knobby tires spin faster and faster, around and around in their driveway with red mud puddles and potholes. They ceremoniously splash and tramp through the potholes, picking up the Seneca's red iron earth. The children's tires are caked with the bloody and rusty earth, and their tires spin and spit magenta and vermilion mud around like an angry, abstract expressionist painter on a bloody tear.

A false God! An Abrahamic idol, a burning man torched
by children on a bike ride. Diana and Craig keep up
their raging rave on their Allegheny desert as ver-
milion-red mud sails through the air. The child's
tornado of communication widens, coming closer to
the fat Dalton walruses on welfare retirement. Bill
and Susan, the blubbering blobs of Allegheny, start
to wonder what is ruining their high as the BMX
Seneca clay starts to baptize *Them,* and much more
damaging, the mud starts to spray their Silver
Bullet beers!

Bill stands up with an air of purpose, but then
starts to wobble after being sprayed with a puddle
of mud water by Craig, "The King" – *De Kooning*. Bill
looks at his new abstract fashion and seems to wonder for a moment about his new metrosexual status.
Bill, with four (4) chins, four (4) beers, and the
inability to do his own laundry, seems confused by
his new avant-garde status. Bill looks lightheaded
and dizzy, and he inadvertently steps backwards,
stumbling back off "*The Raft of Poverty*," and falls
into a nasty kiddie pool filled with green water
and empty beers cans. After the big splash down and
the whooping and hollering from daughter and grandchildren about Grandpa falling into the kiddie pool
dies down, large swarms of black gnats and mosquitos float above Grandpa's head. The kiddie pool's
greenish, brackish, water; the empty beer cans; and
now clouds of agitated gnats and mosquitos remind
me of a demilitarized zone (DMZ). It resembles the
nearby poisonous Superfund site — *Love* Canal — and
it has that same burning plastic, pissy, third-
world Superfund smell. The Daltons' *Love* Canal kiddie pool is the heart of the Empire. The kiddie pool has Grandpa Bill freaking, splashing, and
struggling, and unable to sit up. He believes he
will drown in eight (8) inches of Appalachian piss
water and is spazzing like a man on fire.

Diana and Craig roar with laughter like circling
sharks as their pathetic fat tuna Grandfather falls

off his poverty raft. Big-Daddy Granddad is fair game in poisonous *Love* Canal, Appalachia. The BMX sharks pedal harder and faster as the *Mother's Day Madness* red-devil dust storm on their driveway continues to swirl and gain speed.

Susan, cockeyed before noon and with last night's puke still on her tank top, yawns.... She walks around in her only pair of Walmart (WMT) pink sweatpants ($4.99) that, instead of having the word "JUICY" imprinted vertically down the leg, Susan's say "ANGRY." Susan slowly turns around to see her two (2) buzzing-bee children trying to find their "Mom." But "Home" is what the Empire State napalmed a long time ago.

Susan is still smoking her spliff roach and a Seneca brand cigarette at the same time in the same hand because her other hand firmly and desperately holds onto a tallboy beer. The tan cigarette filter perfectly matches Susan's tanning-salon skin color. The smoldering plastic cigarette filter melts into Susan's nicotine-stained fingers. Susan's fleshy, tan skin slowly melts into a smoking nub that is actually her fingers.

Susan tries to take a drag on her tobacco-less fingers and instead physically and metaphysically blows a goodbye kiss to her children by attempting to smoke her own fingers. With one eye closed and one open — the Dalton woman's evil eye focuses. Susan closes one eye, cursing, trying to swat away her imagined wasps flying next to her - that are in fact her children. Susan, a mother, seems unable to comprehend that her children are trying to communicate with her.

The pink and black BMX bikes swim and swirl in the orbit or ocean of an iron dust devil. From within this third-eye hurricane, one faintly hears: "Happy Mother's Day, Happy Mother's Day, Happy Mother's Day," slowing cresting with an unassuming crescendo and then sinking back into the whitecapped waves like a shark fin slowly gliding up and down on the surface of water. Diana and Craig's duet duel turns into a quartet as their singing coaxes the wanton groans of drowning seamen who leave for work at sea and never dock in a safe harbor again. Sailors and children looking for their mothership on the far-off horizon within the vast ocean. Diana and Craig's illbient song is a lonely shanty from the bottom of the cold Atlantic. It sounds like Herman Melville's "Billy in the Darbies" from his play "Billy Budd" has been remixed by Aphex Twin and/or User 18081971 into an illbient serenade for mothers.

Their song's bass line charges ahead, fueled by a hornet's steady and mean revenge. The children chorus together, "Erreeennn, Errreeennn, Erreeennn," to warm up and ratchet up the situation. Both children in falsettos start singing like angels, "Happy Mother's Day... Happy Mother's Day... Happy Mother's Day...." The singing trails off, then their bassy, not just ambient but illbient "Erreeennn, Errreeennn, Erreeennn" returns like a fast and menacing machine or train, "Erreeennn, Errreeennn, Erreeennn."

Quickly, the singsong returns to the falsettos, "Happy Mother's Day... Happy Mother's Day... Happy Mother's Day...." Then, following, there is a long chorus crash-up or mash-up: "EEERRRRRREEEEEEEENNNN!"

Only Diana the archer correctly hits the falsetto notes in a solo "Happy Mother's Day...."

Craig interrupts and complements her solo with his own solo of "EEERRRRRREEEEEEEENNNN!" that echoes about as Diana butters it up with "Happy Mother's Day...." Then, quickly "EEERRRRRREEEEEEEENNNN!" It is a talky, singsong acapella musical called "*Mother's Day Madness*"!

"EEERRRRRREEEEEEEENNNN!" "Happy Mother's Day...." 1
"EEERRRRRREEEEEEEENNNN!" "Happy Mother's Day...." 2
"EEERRRRRREEEEEENNNN!" 3

  4

Susan seems to start to hallucinate that her chant- 5
ing children are wasps and grabs the bug spray can 6
of Raid. She knocks over her suntan oil, four (4) 7
empty beer cans, and a bag of cheesy puffs that fall 8
and litter her one-hundred-and-fifty (150) square- 9
foot "Raft of Poverty." Susan unfortunately turns 10
the nozzle of the bug-spray facing towards her 11
instead of facing away from her in her left hand. 12
This is where Susan Dalton lives and excels. Susan 13
flings her burning cigarette butt at her children 14
and slowly tries to stand, waving at the imaginary 15
hornets flying around her. The children hornets 16
want to pollinate with their poison. Their mother 17
is a dank, dark, awkward woman with blind-spots — 18
perfect for the location of a hornet's nest. Susan 19
stumbles towards her finale, swings around with her 20
arms wildly flailing at the imaginary fighter jet 21
hornets. 22

  23

Susan focuses her one good eye in order to spray 24
those wasps she seems to hear in her mind. And she 25
knows a big swill of beer will help with this task. 26
The buzzing BMX tumbleweeds that are her crying and 27
laughing children continue to circle Susan like 28
sharks feeding on a dead whale. 29

  30

A big swill of beer for Susan enables her to open 31
one good eye. It opens for a clipped moment in 32
order to temporarily drive a car correctly, light 33
a cigarette correctly, or not fall on her face and 34
break her nose, which has happened three (3) times 35
during the last six (6) years. Susan reaches for 36
her Silver Bullet beer on the table in order to cool 37
her vampire heart, but instead, she falls, blowing 38
up the cheesy puffs again and sending the orange 39
carcinogen puffs all over her "Raft of Poverty." 40
Orange puff bombs land on the deck and float hap- 41
pily in Grandpa's green *Love* Canal kiddie pool. 42

During Susan's physical slide, scrape, and rebound, she gracefully scoops up her beer in her right hand and turns it upside down above her head, allowing the beer to waterfall lovingly around her mouth, face, hair, and body.

The drenched, stumbling welfare Queen steps this way and that, as Susan is now in a wet T-shirt contest. Accordingly, her Appalachian next-door neighbor yells over the fence, "Show me your tits."

Susan throws her empty Silver Bullet beer can at her neighbor and concentrates on the task at hand. The window of focusing opportunity is fast approaching for Susan now as the alcohol surges in her blood-stream, and she has little time to decide and/or perform a bodily action with accuracy. Susan raises the Raid bug spray with a stiff and rigid arm with the nozzle still pointed at herself, one and a half (1 1/2) feet away from her once beautiful light blue / green eyes that were once speckled with fun golden slivers.

Susan focuses on the rolling tumbleweed wasp nests that are her children, that sing a tune Susan cannot understand. Susan screams to her father, "What are the wasps saying? Happy Birthday? Happy Easter? Happy Memorial Day? Happy what the fuck day are they saying?"

Susan screeches from the bottom of her mommy vampire soul, "Shut the fuck up — take this, mother-fuckers." She sprays at full pressure a steady jet stream of Raid hornet killer with a spray range of twenty (20) feet directly into her eyes, which were once the baby-blue window to her innocent child soul.

The spectracide, with a dielectric voltage of fifty thousand (50,000) volts able to wipe out entire nests of wasps and hornets, blinds Susan instantly. Susan then frantically runs into the side of the house instead of the open door. Then she runs into a tree and falls. Then Mother runs into the house of the neighbor who wanted to see her tits and falls.

Susan rants and repeats some insane mantra. She continues to rub her eyes as she runs into a few cars right in front of me. Then she bounces off my Ford Interceptor, looking into the blacked-out windows as a mirror. She looks directly at me, but she is not *looking* directly at me. Susan alternately whispers and giggles to herself, "I can see - hee, hee, hee - I can see - hee, hee, hee - I can see."

I could scrutinize Susan's burned-out and melted-out eye sockets as she fixes her hair in my Empire car windows. She is about to go into "Shock" as the convulsing in between seizures increases. Susan slowly paws her way past me, blindly and desperately walking down the street, bouncing off the other parked cars. Still giggling and whispering words as if she is sharing a long-suppressed secret: "I can see, I can see, I can see.... I can see, I can see, I can see...."

Dear Family Court and Good Reader, I'm witnessing Susan's demise... it is a live rat-lab test, and I am a two (2) way mirror; I am an unreliable variable, a blockade, a closed door. This rat test is a nuclear, biological, and chemical (NBC) warfare test. I pull up my satellite bird's-eye view and Susan looks like a rat bouncing off test doors, wandering down the road she grew up on, looking for her truth, looking for her *Other,* looking for her remedy after swallowing her poison.

Chapter 16

2:53 P.M. - <u>A MOTHER'S STORY WITHIN</u>
<u>LUXURY, OR, COMPLAINT #21-6154</u>

I drive back to Highland Avenue and park in my inconspicuous spot. From one of many screens, I see Madeline McHugh in her Florida room. She knits and weaves one of her many fashion projects that terrify her relatives. Crocheted scarves and doilies, woven sweaters and knitted hats and mittens round out Maddy's woven fashion lines. All these knitted "Gifts" from Madeline year-round are a busy hobby for Maddy, but no one ever wears anything she creates. For endless hours, days, years, Mad spins a yarn; she sculpts with needles and yarn — making clothes for her friends and family. This woven web suffocates her "*Loved*" victims. There are scarves woven with wooly thorns that incessantly scratch faces and necks. There are sweaters with three (3) arms that had the shape of garbage bags. Always in the making are turtlenecks with V-necks, pants with different leg lengths, and pants with no ass or no hip. These *Gifts* made all of Mad's friends and family very uneasy around holidays and birthdays. Madeline is like the Snookys and Ivanka Trumps from New Jersey who fancy themselves fashion designers

even though they are really fashion buying and mer-
chandising (FBM) dropouts.

Madeline, and lots of other "Mothers," dropped out
of college prior to Roe vs. Wade (1973) because
they went to one of those sudden and hasty "Taking
a Year-Off" camps for "Good" rich girls.   One of
those "Camps" for Jewish and Christian princesses
to leave no trace of mistakes before 1973. This
"Women Camp" ages these fair young ladies three
hundred (300) years in nine (9) months, and so in
reality, these young women never come back... and
this is a major maxim of *Mother's Day Madness*.

Madeline's housekeeper, Hoi-Noi, is blowing hot
air into Maddy's emotional balloon with her broken
English, "I *love* the colors and how they like, they
like, they like, they like..."

The Vietnamese and Asians in general when not speaking their native tongue and speak English have a
linguistic speech habit that is quite contagious
and sounds like a skipping record increasing in
time or beats per minute (BPM). The volume also
increases as everyone raids the ancient temple and/
or today's birthday party celebration. A celebration of armies chasing ghosts with cannons or mats
of firecrackers. Hoi-Noi is smoking-gun powder and
smoldering Chinese paper — colorful red, blue, and
green patterns on fire, smoldering and fun. Hoi-
Noi is slowly burning in the smoky background as
Madeline's hair is on fire — glowing like a Palm
Beach Medusa. Maddy is subconsciously screaming,
"Light it up! Light it up! Light it up!" even
though Mad's bleach-blond hair is already ablaze.

Hoi-Noi's vocal freak-out, like with many of the
Asian languages, is tonal specific in that different intonations / pronunciations mean different
words or phrases. Therefore, Hoi-Noi singsongs,
always insinuating through a sixth (6th) sense and/
or an audio sense - a question and/or a statement,

but it doesn't work well in the English / American
mouth or mind. Americans, especially, don't want to
be sold the voodoo of intonation. Americans "Say
what they mean and mean what they say."

I can see that Hoi-Noi is trying to bullshit a bull-
shitter (Madeline). But many Asians since World War
II and Vietnam seem to not be sure whether they're
allowed to tell the truth about happiness anymore.
I don't blame *Them* – atomic bombs and napalm can
put a crimp in your *truth* game, your *Real* game,
and/or your mother game.

Hoi-Noi tries to speak, "I *love* the colors and
how they like blee-blel-bleeellll-lend with the
background." "Blend" and/or "Ble" blocks her phonetically from communicating with Maddy's ear.
Then Hoi-Noi gets lost in, "They-like, they-like,
they-like, they-like," which sounds like a raging pachinko parlor game. Hoi-Noi gets stuck in
the drive-through franchise and linguistically
explodes with, "They-like, they-like, they-like,
they-like," as if she is a multi-stage Roman Candle
exploding into multiple colors in the sky. Hoi-Noi
phonetically explodes in all primary colors and
then falls quickly to the ground in cascading smoky
white trails.

Most Americans don't get excited about the gray
kabuki theater of intonation. Hoi-Noi and other
English-speaking Asians turn into stuttering
pachinko pinballs and end up swinging and hanging
from the rafters in America with a cigarette in
their mouth and their hand of cards very close to
their vest. Their life savings is usually on the
line, and they're standing on the Mahjong betting
table screaming, samurai-style, "They-like, they-
like, they-like, they-like."

Madeline looks over at Hoi-Noi and articulates the
word slowly, "Bbblllleeennnddd," as if she were
talking to a brain-dead dog.

Madeline knows the word Hoi-Noi is trying to pro-
nounce is "Blend" because she told Hoi-Noi yesterday that she herself "*Loved* the colors and how
they, like, blend into the background." Madeline,
angry now that she has to teach Hoi-Noi how to mimic
and parrot her again, thinks for a quick, deep, and
deadly moment. Mad continues to needle her current webby creation and disapprovingly glares at
Hoi-Noi. Mad gazes deep into Hoi-Noi's eyes with a
furrowed brow and a cat-like scowl. Mad then seems
to think to herself as she smirks at Hoi-Noi: *Maybe
I need to get better illegal immigrant maid help.*

The average pay for illegal immigrants in this Empire
State area is approximately twenty ($20) dollars an
hour, tax free. The average for an America mother
in the Empire is twelve dollars and twenty cents
($12.20) an hour (take-home pay after Empire taxes
is eight dollars and thirty-five cents ($8.35)).

Hoi-Noi seems to feel this horrible "Getting fired"
/ jobless thought and shows Madeline with her pale
and shell-shocked face. Hoi-Noi turns white as a
ghost; she is frozen and terrified as Maddy becomes
warm and delighted.

Madeline's delights are only, and always, momentary
and monetary. Madeline gets back on the anxious-
train all "Good mommies" seem to feign these days.
Today, like every day, Madeline seems "Super anxious" about getting a lunchtime phone call from her
oldest daughter, Margaret. Margaret is a housewife
married to a doctor with two (2) children and a
third (3rd) child on the way. Margaret is Madeline's
Real. Margaret is a feminine soldier for Madeline,
a soldier of marriage, a soldier of the idolized
virgin mother, a mercenary mother. Margaret is an
obedient slave and/or subject to Madeline the *Red-
Queen.* Margaret does not question authority – she
is scared of it. Margaret has given up on being /
doing anything (or maybe she never tried) with her

life and has had child after child, immediately after marrying her high school sweetheart.

Madeline's motherly enslavement of Margaret is not a rearing, but a brainwashing. Margaret seems too scared to question her mother, and that is no Empire child mistake. Margaret continues to strive, continues to carry the torch to enhance her patriarchy pedigree as some country-club cunt who only marries well so if she has to - she can divorce even better.

The only life, it seems, for these nuns of pump and obedient daughters of dump is to forsake their own lives by coveting and parasitically imperializing and policing everyone around *Them* with *Mother's Day Madness* and/or *the Expectant Mother Racket.*

The more money / freedom that Madeline and Margaret have within "Family *love*," the more inadequate they both feel. The deep neurosis of *Motherhood* is a nagging vertigo both women suppress by parroting each other to seem more familiar, or just not alone. Margaret is exactly what Madeline is, exactly what the Empire State budget dictates all women should be: The *Real* - barefoot and pregnant, in the kitchen on the phone, chatting with nice girlfriends about good diapers, good husbands, and good shopping. As Joseph Swetnam wrote in his 1615 "Arraignment of Women":

> The Arraignment of Leuud, Idle, Froward, and
> Unconstant Women: Or The Vanitie of Them,
> Choose You Whether: With a Commendation of
> Wise, Vertuous and Honest Women: Pleasant for
> Married Men, Profitable for Young Men, and
> Hurtfull To None.

Madeline is hurtful to everyone because Madeline is hurtful to herself. This makes all her "*Love*," help, or "Gift-*Love*" toxic. Margaret is Madeline's Gift-*Love* child; Margaret is her favorite child, and she is exactly what Madeline wanted to be twenty

(20) years prior. Margaret was bought as an *Adopted* vehicle for Madeline to relive her youth without mistakes — an American idol! Margaret is manically happy to be a child-whore / a fan for heli-moms and Maddy. But Mad is an Only-Fan Mommy, a Me-Generation Mommy, a "Good" Baby-Boomer mother... an oxymoron mother.

Margaret presents a false image – a Virgin Mary, "Happy to please everyone" in a perverted, patriarchal sense. The Holy Virgin veil... the hollowed-out woman is Madeline, just like the Veil of Madeline. Madeline is *The Veil*, the *Mother*, or the *Innocent Child* is a control-fraud sold to the religious masses; it's an opiate sold to Queeny Dads and/or masculine Marms on their own psychotic Holy Crusade. I'm reminded of our very American Founding Father Roger Williams, who declared in 1636, as he established Providence, Rhode Island: "Religion is the rape of the soul."

It would be easy to say that Margaret has worked so hard at being just like Madeline, her mother, because of the weekly direct deposits of one thousand eight hundred dollars ($1,800) Madeline deposits into Margaret's savings account. Living the country-club life on a young doctor's salary ($140,000) on the Upper West Side of Manhattan is tough. So, besides the weekly allowance, there are "Celebrations of our *love*," shopping-sprees, and "Because I *love* you" purchases of dresses, automobiles, vacations, and more dresses. The annual total of Madeline's "*Love*" for Margaret is around fifty-one thousand dollars ($51,000). It would be too crass to say this "*Love*" is pork-barreled extortion or maternal bribery, but within my old Air Force *Intelligence* Unit spying on corrupt political families stealing from the government or people in Nicaraguan or Afghanistan, these Madeline pay-offs would be classified as "A criminal racket" that "Aides and abets child abuse criminal activity." Here in the

white-devil Empire State of New York bribes and
extortion, it is called "*Love.*"

Madeline cannot sit still anymore. She paces back
and forth in her kitchen wondering why Margaret,
her daughter, has not called yet. Maddy cleans the
countertop for the third (3rd) time even though
her housekeeper Hoi-Noi has cleaned and bleached
the kitchen twice earlier in the day upon Maddy's
instructions. Mad's heart is racing and can only be
tempered by the sociopathic delusions she received
from one of her spoiled children or lapdogs.

The phone rings, but it is one of thirty-nine (39)
mobile phones on the kitchen island in a large,
round bowl. The bowl glows with a cosmic digital
radiance. The cellular bowl looks like a hologram
planet from another galaxy. This phone planet is
eclipsing the sun - the phone planet is eclipsing the
Other. The cellular planet has the data and whoever
controls the data - controls the world. Madeline
grabs at one of the twenty (20) stray mobile phones,
five (5) flip phones, six (6) Blackberries, four
(4) house-phones, and/or another four (4) shortwave
radio intercom phones that may be ringing in the
kitchen bowl data planet.

Madeline cradles the telecommunication instruments
with an average price of eight-hundred and seventy-
eight dollars ($878) and yells, "Margaret, hello?
Margaret? Margaret, hello? Margaret, is that you?"

A language, a painting, a poem, a dance, a communication tool, a phone rings in the pile of family
telephones totaling thirty-six thousand three hundred sixty-four dollars ($36,364). But the phone
Madeline speaks into isn't the phone that is ringing. Madeline slams it down, and the phone slides
easily across the fine and slippery marble island
top. Madeline grabs one of the flip phones and tries
to communicate with that phone, but she throws it
in the garbage when she realizes no one is on the

phone. Maddy then grabs a house phone and starts pushing buttons as the house security system introduces itself as "Peggy" and talks to Madeline in a robotic voice with a posh English accent.

Peggy the robot says, "Hello, Madeline, how may I help you? My name is Peggy."

Their conversation is now being amplified throughout Madeline's twelve-thousand (12,000) square-foot house on the phone intercom system with interspersed beeps and squelching feedback as Madeline struggles to control herself and her communications. One of the phones rings in the earth data planet.... Madeline yells at the house phone, and her entire house gets way too much information. This audio narrative or portrait of Madeline is being projected from every room in the house and from every accessory structure, garage, pool house, and horse barn on the forty (40) acre property. Here, on Mother's Day, even Peter the pool man cleaning the pool three hundred (300) feet from the house gets too much information via the intercom in the pool house.

Madeline truly speaks from her heart and asks in her *Mother's Day Madness* language, "Peggy? What kind of Mary Poppins bullshit name is that? Fuck you, Peggy Poppins!!! Fuck You!!!! Fucking phones.... I hate these fucking phones!"

Peggy the robot asks politely, "Hello, Madeline, what would you like to do with the fucking phones?" in a perfect British Broadcasting (BBC) feminine voice.

Madeline, ignoring Peggy the robot, desperately pleads, "Margaret, are you there? Margaret? Margaret? Please hold on!"

Madeline pushes more buttons on another of her thirty-nine (39) phones. Alas, the mechanical window shades in the entire house start coming down, accompanied by a warning alarm that sounds like a whip-poor-will nightbird. The shade alarm sings: "Whip-poor-will, whip-poor-will, whip-poor-will." Then the shades start going back up, and the shade alarm rings in a higher tone and repeats twice as fast: "Whip-poor-will, whip-poor-will, whip-poor-will, whip-poor-will, whip-poor-will, whip-poor-will." Then the shades come back down the whole way, and it gets very, very dark inside Madeline's house.

Madeline slowly starts to become self-aware and asks, "Shit... fuck... what the hell is the matter with me?"

Peggy the Empire snot-bot asks, "Hello, Madeline, would you like help with your *shit-fuck*? Hello, Madeline, can I help you with your *What the hell's a matter with me?*"

Peggy, in perfect British English continues, "My name is Peggy; I'm here to make everyone happy. Madeline, are you still happy? Madeline, how can I make you happy?" In the background, Peggy disc jockeys (DJs) Bobby McFerrin's "Don't Worry Be Happy," but the CD gets stuck on the musical intro. The finger clapping / whistling introduction is great, and then the pleasant lyrics start with the descending falsetto harmony-hook:

Ooh, ooh-ooh-ooh-ooh-ooh-ooh-ooh-ooh.

Ooh-ooh-ooh-ooh.

Ooh-ooh-ooh.

Peggy the posh DJ gets the track stuck on maybe twenty (20) beats per minute (BPM), so the cheerful melodic song turns into a glitchy dirge. This illbient bad-trip with Bobby singing down way too many octaves is approaching the most Non-Commercial

Potential (NCP) soundscape known to sound-wave cos-
monauts on the frequency modulation (FM) dial. The
"Ohh-ooh-oohs" stick and then sonically and metaphysically turn Madeline's *Real* into the soundtrack
for an Appalachian chainsaw massacre.

One of the thirty-nine (39) phones starts ringing
again. Madeline reaches aimlessly into the cellular black-hole bowl and grabs another phone in a
belligerent and arrogant manner. She answers conde-
scendingly in a cunty tone, "Hello? Hello? God...
fucking... dammit!"

Peggy, again with a *lovely* "Bathe" England voice
asks, "Hello, Madeline, how can I help you today
with *God Fucking*? Would you like to see today's
sales on Amazon for God Fucking?"

Madeline screams a shrill, murderous shriek that
raises the hair on the back of Peter the pool guy's
neck, who is hiding out by the pool house. Madeline
continues crying, blubbering, "Why me? Why me? Why
me?" She punches the black planet earth data bowl
and knocks it to the floor. Very expensive communication devices scatter around the white marble
floor. These communication tools worth thirty-six
thousand three hundred sixty-four dollars ($36,364)
within a luxurious lifestyle and representing the
finest communication tools money can buy - did not
communicate to anyone.

Peggy, the royalist redcoat in hiding, the robotic
female concierge service asks Madeline, "Hello,
Madeline, how can I help you with your *Why me,
why me, why me?* My name is Peggy; I'm here to make
everyone happy and tell the truth."

One of the thirty-nine (39) phones on the kitchen
floor is still ringing... Madeline, crying and
bawling now, picks up an iPhone 14 worth almost
thirteen hundred ($1,300) dollars and speaks into
the dead phone with dead air, "Why do this to me on

People's Exhibit M - A Bowl of Phones Worth Thirty-Six Thousand Dollars ($36,000)

Mother's Day? Why? Why? Why, Peggy, on Mother's
Day? Why on Mother's Day?"

I think, *Wow... Madeline has Constant Perseverance,
but she isn't going anywhere... which, per Einstein,
equals insanity*. I think... *I need to remember
that one*. I write out those words on a small pink
Post-It and put it on my dashboard. "Going nowhere
within constant perseverance is INSANITY!"

Peggy interrupts Madeline's existential question
as Bobby McFerrin "oohs" politely and professionally. She asks, "Pardon me, Madeline, but would
you like a Coupon Code for *Why-Me? Why-Me? Why-Me?*
I can give you a fifty (50) percent discount at
Walmart (WMT) today on *Why Me*."

Madeline throws the iPhone she has to her ear down
on the kitchen granite countertop, and it hops,
skips, and bounces nicely into the kitchen sink
filled with water and sudsy white foam. As the
sleek chrome phone vanishes into the watery bubble
bath, a few tiny white bubbles float up towards
Madeline's face. Maddy smiles and giggles for a
psychotic moment, and then she whispers to no one
in particular, "Bubbles... I like bubbles...."

After a few moments of calm silence, a determined
phone rings incessantly. Maddy slowly is turning
red. Mad makes scary faces and strange noises as
she becomes unhinged. Mad seems to retreat into her
own mind. Mad stares ahead, lost within insanity.

Madeline brings one phone, then a second, then a
third mobile phone to her mouth, yelling, "Margaret,
Margaret, Margaret! Where are you?"

Peggy, the female concierge service, misunderstands
Mad and asks her in a pleasant Shakespearean voice,
"Hello, Madeline, wherefore art thou?"

The fourth (4th) mobile phone rises to life, beeping

and flashing. Madeline wrestles with it like a live fish trying to get back home underwater. Maddy grabs the fishy flip-phone with both hands and carefully opens up the older phone, slowly and carefully.

"Mommy? Mommy, is that you?" Margaret asks in a winded and whiny tone acceptable for some eight (8) year-olds in some immature cultures.

Madeline is suddenly orgasmic and alive again (even though she hasn't had an orgasm in twenty (20) years) and asks Margaret breathlessly, "Are you okay?"

Margaret usually calls, texts, emails, tweets, Snapchats, and/or Facebooks her mother on an average of once every one (1) hour. They last texted each other last night (ten (10) hours ago) and once this morning via their matching nine hundred and fifty dollar ($950) iPhones. Texting on the McHugh "Family Plan" costs approximately two thousand two hundred dollars ($2,200) a month in telephone charges.

Margaret assures her mother, "Yeah, I'm fine; I told you I had a company dinner with Steve's office last night. I told you I'd be up late and sleeping in. What took you so long time to answer the phone? Are you okay?"

Madeline sheepishly answers, "Yeah, I was just busy cooking here for Mother's Day dinner."

Margaret grease-guns back, "I know, Mommy, and Happy Mother's Day!" as the squeaky wheel of "Empire *Love*" is oiled and silenced.

"Thank you, and Happy Mother's Day to you, also!" Madeline exudes.

This *Mother's Day Madness* merry-go-round is making me motion sick. I turn away from the screens and look out the window. I think about the *Mother's Day Madness* merry-go round, and I think about the last

letter I received from my Grandmother Anna Jarvis
after she was institutionalized by the Floral and
Candy Industries nine (9) months before she died
in 1948.

Connie,

*I have a new friend who lives in the room
next door. She has not abandoned me like
you! Did you file the Appeal of my copyright infringement case against Hallmark
cards? Against FTD? My new friend is in
the white-room with nothing in it — I like
that room. How are the rabbits doing? My new
friend is so funny. Did you file the Appeal
of my institutionalization? My friend calls
herself the other nothing or Sister X. The
funny farm is not funny. She only answers
all my questions with the other or nothing.
I ask my new friend lots of questions. Was
that the wind? For Mother's Day next year,
we will plan a large rally in Philadelphia
again! Did you clean up the shit in the rab-
bit pen? I think I'm losing the strength
to write. I think I'm losing the strength
to think clearly... I'm nervous. You hav-
en't visited me. Have you filed the Appeal to
release me? The doctors are drugging me....
The twenty ($20) dollars I lent you on the
way to your first day of college... well,
I wish you would thank me. Did I tell you
about my new friend? Today she is nothing.
Tell me about the rabbits... is Lenny still
fat and cute? On other days, my new friend
is the other. The doctors are raping me. My
new friend said, "I was adorable." I said,
"I am adorable." She is strange; I like them
all — I wish I knew more about her. I asked
my new friend the other, "What does my room
look like from the outside?" The other said,
"It looks like nothing." I said, "Don't be
silly; the doctor's friends are raping me all*

night long; it has to look like something."
My friend said again, "You look like noth-
ing." Please file the Appeals — I'm dying.
My new friend the other said, "It's only the
wind." My new friend nothing next door said,
"I'm going to fuck you!" My other new friend
Sister X said, "You're my only friend. I feel
like someone. You know, Connie... it is all
a wasteland... and appearance is everything.
I have a confession to make: I like to be
adored. Tell me about the wind again; I think
she is my only friend.

Love is NOT Affectionate, nor does Love Last
For, For, Forever,

Grandma Anna

Madeline and Margaret continue to talk about the
dresses other women were wearing last night, what
their good children and grandchildren were wearing, good shopping finds, and good food they like
to eat. Everything these mothers discuss involves
money being spent that they did not earn. A mother's
existence where the children are bought, shelved,
isolated, abstract, alien, and ghostly. Mothers
discuss money well spent on training or buying their
Emperor or Empress in training a better spot in the
apple-polisher Empire State. There is no thought
of morality, inner happiness, or the future....
For these mothers, if money isn't being spent, it
is "Weird" or not "Family-Friendly." The horrific
lack of common sense and vanity of these mothers
unable to comprehend math, matheme, mathesis, and/
or the metaphysics of child abuse is evidence of a
subhuman mother.

Chapter 17

4:42 P.M. - MOTHER MEETS THE WOMEN OF ALLEGHENY AT THE MOO-MOO, OR, COMPLAINT #21-4532 AND COMPLAINT #21-6154

I am en route to Barbara Dalton's for surveillance on Complaint #21-4532, but my GPS trackers pick-up this accused mother leaving her address, and she becomes a moving blip on my screen coming towards me. At the same time, Madeline McHugh is in transit as another blip on my screen, and both mothers pass me in their cars. The blinking-blips on my screen are my targets, and they visually look like a heat-seeking missile and a crosshaired target about to hit.

Or maybe Mrs. Dalton and Mrs. McHugh are charged magnets... the same size... the same dimension, fighting at first, yet swinging and slapping together hard and forevermore as smashed atoms in a collider.

Barbara and Madeline are the same age and have grown up in Allegheny (population 1,856) their whole lives and have never said more than one (1) sentence to one another. They both knew of each other but don't want to know each other. Their disgust for one another was incarnated during a 1960s

Cold War nuclear bomb emergency drill. These drills were called "Duck and Cover" because children had to hide-out underneath their school desks during these drills, which is when our two (2) Appalachian mothers said one (1) sentence to each other.

It was approximately fifty-five (55) years ago after their first-grade teacher, Ms. Center, scolded *Them* both for not helping each other during the nuclear bomb alarm drill. Ms. Center said, "Now be nice to each other – don't be brats."

So, Madeline turned to Barb and said, "Whatcha looking at?"

Barb retorted in a derogatory tone, "Nothing much.... In fact, nothing at all."

To Barbara, Madeline was a rich country-club cunt who was as much an enemy to her and America as the Seneca Indian or the British royalist-loyalist were. To Madeline, Barbara was a one-eyed troll who was lucky to be allowed to live down there by the swamp on Dam Road.

As our God / Creator / Maker seems to have a sense of humor, our delusions become our reality and our reality becomes our delusion when we least expect it. As I wrote earlier,

"Those that Findeth *Intel* Will Looseth *Intel*."

Both blipping women on my GPS screens seem to be headed for the local gas /convenience store called the "Moo-Moo." Here on Mother's Day, the collision of delusion and reality at the Moo-Moo, with its appropriate vulture logo, there will be a spectac-ular site for the women of Allegheny.

Both Barbara and Madeline have to run errands, and both seem to be running low on gas before their Mother's Day dinners. Barbara still drives her 1976 baby-blue Ford Pinto that is a mutant vehicle: funny, obscene, antiquated, and the *Real*. Barbara's car is more of a cute, unexploded grenade from World War II (2) that Big-Daddy Grandpa keeps on his mantle in case the new neighbors get out of hand. Barbara is a burning woman smoking a Seneca cigarette and rolls slowly in her rusted and rotted-out baby-blue Pinto.

In counterpoint, Madeline drives her brand-new 2021 sky-blue Mercedes station wagon that is more of an Empire State trickle-down fuck-you fashion accessory on four wheels than an automobile. A Benz, a Nazi not hiding in America: like I wrote earlier, Family Court and Dear Reader, the enemy is not scorched from the earth, the defeated loser is put to work or *Adopted* as a human fashion accessory and/or a human social accessory.

Barbara comes in from the east side of the Moo-Moo gas station, and Madeline comes in from the west. In the center row of gas pumps, there is only one (1) available pump that both Barbara and Madeline see at the same moment. They are both stopped by a small school bus backing out of the Moo-Moo convenience store area. Madeline and Barbara jostle and jockey like race car drivers on the starting loop at a National Association of Stock Car Auto Racing (NASCAR) car race.

The baby-blue Pinto inches up to the navy-blue Benz and tailgates... Barb bumps the Benz! Mad, in turn, pumps her brakes, and the Pinto slams into the rear of Maddy's Mercedes. The Benz then tries to take the inside lane, trying to see which direction the bus will take. The Pinto, in reply, squeezes the Benz into the turn, and Madeline chokes - she brakes. Barb revs her Pinto as plumes of black exhaust pollute the Moo-Moo parking lot. Barb yells, "Fuck you, rich bitch!" On cue, her little car that-maybe-could backfires! And the women of Allegheny jump!

Mad's Benz pulls back as she contemplates her next move... The world spins faster, as the last of the NASCAR starting laps spins faster and then the green flag is waved, and the Allegheny Moo-Moo falls into wonderful Americana chaos.

The annual Moo-Moo Demolition Derby race started decades ago because two (2) mothers suffering badly from *Mother's Day Madness* always raced and fought on Mother's Day for a Moo-Moo gas pump (Regular Self-Serve Gas - 87: $3.39 a Gallon, or Full Serve Super Gas - 92: $4.20 a Gallon). The pressure of American *Motherhood* and Mother's Day is too much for Appalachian women... so henceforth, the annual Allegheny Mother's Day Moo-Moo Demolition Derby takes place on Mother's Day.

The small yellow school bus pulls back slowly, singing its steady reversal song in triplets, "Beep-beep-beep, beep-beep-beep, beep-beep-beep." And for some strange reason, I start hearing that Bobby McFerrin song. The chorus of "Don't Worry Be Happy" echoes and mimics the "Beep-beep-beep." This Moo-Moo cacophony is contemporary Appalachian music... it is handsome, mesmerizing, and seems to slow time –

Ooh, ooh-ooh-ooh-ooh-ooh-ooh-ooh-ooh.

Beep, beep-beep-beep-beep-beep-beep-beep-beep.

Ooh-ooh-ooh-ooh.

Beep-beep-beep-beep.

Ooh-ooh-ooh.

Beep-beep-beep.

The women of Allegheny start to really stare, point, and gather. They look and glare... with a scorned-woman's gaze. Oh my God, (OMG) the women of

Allegheny have a professional's pout. The women of
Allegheny frown – the Moo-Moo cashier stops counting
the money. The women of Appalachia grin painfully
out of their car windows; the women of Allegheny
curse in senior-citizen and World-War II (2) languages. The frightened women of Allegheny look out
from the Moo-Moo store windows, transfixed.

Barbara and Madeline snarl at each other like ferocious fighters in the coliseum ring.

Beep, beep-beep-beep-beep-beep-beep-beep-beep.

Ooh-ooh-ooh-ooh.

The bus continues rolling backwards and forwards,
but it still does not move more than three (3) feet
either way. Barb and Mad negotiate with every inch
as this NASCAR traffic jam continues. The little
yellow submarine navigates by beeping more than
moving. Madeline and Barbara stare at each other,
ready to go full road-rage. The women of Allegheny
start texting and taking videos of the 2021 *Mother's
Day Madness* Moo-Moo Demolition Derby.

The little yellow bus with flashing lights continues to beep and not budge!? The Allegheny mothers
wonder which crazed mother will run over a child in
broad daylight – and on MOTHER'S DAY! The Moo-Moo
parking lot is the new Appalachian Main Street,
and the women of Allegheny can smell a murder coming towards Main Street. Is it going to be Barbara
or Madeline who is going to kill another mother's
child to satisfy their own *Mother's Day Madness*?

Or who, God forbid, who is going to honk? No one
honks in Appalachia – honking is blasphemy in
Allegheny – and it only is done by godless her-
etics. Who would honk these "Children" or "Our
children" out of the way? Other cars are leaving
the old pumps after filling up, and new customers
are pulling in behind. Barbara and Madeline fume

and jockey with the yellow-and-black window-licker wagon. Barbara and Madeline sneer and hiss through reflections of the "Special" school bus. Both mothers have white knuckles and sweaty palms as they heat-up this scrum. One mother grasps a slimy 1976 plastic steering wheel covered with duct tape; the other mother is tight-fisting a 2021 clammy wheel made of high-end mahogany.

The bus driver of the butter-chunk bus, an old haggard townie woman of Allegheny, conveniently doesn't realize she is holding up Moo-Moo traffic. Then the bus driver suddenly realizes that all the children are not on the bus, so the bus pulls forward again into the parking space. The reverse beeping alarm: beep-beep-beep, beep-beep-beep, beep-beep-beep, increases in speed for some reason. The little yellow bus slowly pulls into the parking spot it just partially reversed out of. This very avant-garde gasoline ballet enrages Barb and Maddy into what artsy-fartsy "Artists" call "Performance Art" and/or "A Social Practice."

But down on Main Street, Appalachia, this is just another *Mother's Day Madness* Moo-Moo Demolition Derby.

Adding fuel to the fire during this temporary hiatus of sanity with the special bus is a snarky Chevy. A grandma in a Grady-White pulls into Barbara and Madeline's pump spot. Grandma with faux wood paneling the color of burnt umber in the Grady-White is a false-flag penetrator.

Madeline collapses onto the steering wheel horn of her 2021 ice-blue Mercedes Benz, making everyone in quiet and desperate Allegheny squirm.... The women of Allegheny start to dial the police and call the cops because no one honks their horn in *Upstate*, America. The tone of the Mercedes horn starts to change octaves and creates unique sound waves as it echoes in the small Allegheny valley. The warbler frequency goes from a sawtooth vibrato at a mid-decibel to a reverberating square-wave in numerous high-frequency tones as it bounces, resonates, quantizes, and wanders throughout and around the local hills and hollows of the Southern Tier.

Maddy's blaring car horn spurs Barbara to grip her steering wheel tighter and prime her Pinto. It's the "To-the-Death Moo-Moo Demolition Derby" she's been dreaming about for last two hundred and sixty-nine (269) years. A dreamy demolition derby and the only thing Barbara Dalton would ever be invited to — besides being subpoenaed (legally forced) to bear witness against her daughter Susan in the Empire's Court.

Barbara revs-up her 1976 Ford Pinto improvised explosive device (IED) with a glass-pack muffler system: "Rumble, rumble, rumble, bat, bat, baaaaaat, baaat, bat, bat, rumble, rumble rumble. Bat, bat, baaaaaat, baaat, bat, bat, rumble, rumble rumble." Barbara and her Pinto seem to be digging into the ground like a cornered cat about to attack.

Across from her, Madeline, the dangerous and vindictive sixteen (16) year-old brat lays off her horn and stamps both her feet simultaneously on the gas and the brake pedals of her car. Madeline's Benz revs and brakes at the same time, like a chained bull. Charged, but frozen in her Mercedes: revving, braking, pausing, revving, pausing... high and fast....

Maddy has brought South Los Angles, California, to Appalachia. Mad is a cruising Roja lowrider chola in her Benzy: popping, pimping, ducking, jumping, rolling... low and slow....

Madeline can be a *Red-Queen* cruising the Moo-Moo in Allegheny or Mad can be burning rubber doing donuts at a street takeover with fireworks and a laser show.

Barbara's IED Pinto piñata, her little *Signifier,*
is also making a lot of noise but going nowhere.
The Ford's transmission is slipping so when Barbara
revs up the car and pushes the clutch in, the car
engine starts to sputter as she grinds the gears
into rotating pieces of metal. "Cruncch, crun —
ack, crunch, snaaap, chrunccchh." Barbara continues grinding her gears and sways back and forth,
revving and almost stalling, revving and stalling,
revving and stalling.

Hand-to-hand combat at a Moo-Moo gas pump is not
excessive within the subterfuge / surrogate life
in Nicaragua, Afghanistan, or Appalachia. What I
am looking at — mothers killing each other in the
Empire Year, 2021 — could have been Mississippi
1972, San Salvador 1982, or Kandahar in 2002.

Barbara is revving-up for the clutch-grind, almost
stall, move a foot or so, and then do it all again:
rev-die, rev-die, rev-die.

Mad and Barb's Empire Survival Research Lab (SRL)
performance is a lesson on how NOT to live a motherly life. The women of Allegheny walk out onto the
sidewalk surrounding the big Moo-Moo, shaking their
heads in disapproval. They take down license plate
numbers, names, and notes. They stand around the
Moo-Moo parking lot, watching Barbara and Madeline's
fall from grace while laughing and scowling like
wild hyenas and with the video phones rolling.

The little yellow bus again starts to reverse back
NOT into the Mother's Day Dairy-Queen Demolition
Derby (New England) or the 7-11 *Red-Queen* Demolition
Derby (*Downstate* New York), but the Mother's Day
Moo-Moo Demolition Derby in Appalachia, and it
sounds like this:

Ooh, ooh-ooh-ooh-ooh-ooh-ooh-ooh-ooh-ooh.

Beep, beep-beep- beep-beep-beep-beep-beep-beep.

Ooh-ooh-ooh-ooh.

Beep-beep-beep-beep.

Ooh-ooh-ooh.

Beep-beep-beep.

The women of Allegany start to take bets on which mother (Barbara or Madeline?) was going to lose it first. Was luxury – "The daughter of indolence" – going to win, or will perhaps poverty – with its self-destruction and vicious means – be the new 2021 Queen of the Moo-Moo Demolition Derby? The school bus, the butter-chunk chariot, backs again into Barbara's and Madeline's gas station cross they have to bear. The Moo-Moo sidewalk betting becomes a ferocious trading floor. The Moo-Moo mothers of Allegheny are suddenly active-traders of the patriarchal pump... and fought-against / bet-against, the daughters of the patriarchal dump. The Empire market-maker plays both sides of the bets, and *The Expectant Mother* stock market thrives at the Moo-Moo! It mints immoral mothers called Mary and Eve with faux financial halos and puts out of business / bankrupts "Mr. and Mrs. Ed and Betty Steady."

Madeline takes the yellow bus's direction as a sign from God that children, especially "Special children," should be honored and respected even more these days. So she reverses, allowing the special school bus to pull out safely, redeeming herself from her earlier, embarrassing horn-honking meltdown in front of the ladies of Allegheny. Madeline is in reverse and daydreams about starting a non-profit (501(c)(3)) group to help these "Special children." She dreams about all the fun benefits and lunches she could host. This thought is a fleeting one because as Madeline reverses, she sees on her Mercedes's video screen rearview a small blue Pinto weaving in reverse towards her! It is Barbara Dalton in reverse gear, sailing her baby-blue IED directly towards Madeline.

Barbara is spazzing-out now because Maddy and the
bus are both reversing. Barb thinks the pump space
is still available because Barb has no side-mir-
rors or rearview mirrors – Barb can only see in
front of her when driving and/or living. Poverty
has no room for the past or tangents that don't
involve food, clothing, and shelter. Barbara also
still cannot get her Pinto into any gear besides
reverse. Barbara, in reverse, is circumventing the
Moo-Moo parking lot, trying to get to the middle
island again. But instead, she comes ass-to-ass
with Madeline's Benz. Mad is now reversing to protect and allow her newly *Adopted "Special Children"*
to safely leave the Moo-Moo Derby.

Barbara grinds her teeth and doesn't give a fuck –
she is in perfect Pinto position to take Madeline
and this Moo-Moo life to the other-side. Madeline
and Barbara, both in reverse, are also both smoking
cigarettes. They both now inch closer to Grandma in
the Grady-White who is finishing up her petroleum
fill-up. Maddy looks like she's feeling goofy and
charitably entitled, so she honks at the granny in
the Grady-White and does so with her hands up in
the air, questioning Grandma in the faux woody car-
avan with a "What the fuck" (WTF) look.

Granny in the Grady-White gets upset, yelling more
1960s Baby-Boomer curse words at Madeline, and then
she gives the finger to Madeline and drives off in
a huff. But Granny forgets to pull out the gas-pump
nozzle from her tank before she pulls away. The gas
hose snaps, and out pours the gasoline. Gasoline
gushes all around, gushing, flammable, flowing,
yellow-like, piss-orange kerosene. The smell is
erotic and powerful, yet the fuel / the energy
plays like a child splishing and splashing.

The world is changing, and mothers now will set
you on fire. Gasoline, a smell heavenly and hellish at the same time flows into the Moo-Moo parking
lot and around Madeline's and Barbara's cars. The

Red-Queens of poverty and luxury smile at each other
as the gasoline *ante* brings this year's Mother's Day
Moo-Moo Demolition Derby to a new height. The women
of Allegheny run for the hills, calling 911 – the
women of Allegheny have seen enough....

Barbara and Madeline still glare at each other in
reverse gear with reverse lights and brake lights
flickering / talking to each other in another language. The mothers talk in tongues. They howl, clat-
ter, chatter, squeal, buck, ruff, and yodel in alien
conversations like my Grandma Anna when she would chop
off wounded soldiers' legs. The *Red-Queens'* hair of
both poverty and luxury slowly becomes aglow... the
Red-Queens' hair slowly becomes aflame. The flames
rise and fill their cars as their eyes stay locked.
Hell hath no fury.... The fires ripple and dance and
slowly start shapeshifting into snakes. Medusa has
arrived at the 2021 Mother's Day Moo-Moo Demolition
Derby, and she is pissed!

Snakes, lizards, serpents, and walking reptilians
rise up from their chariot vehicles: racer snakes
pop out of the Pintos grille as multiple anacondas
symmetrically rise from the Mercedes-Benz wheel
wells. Rattlers coil on the roofs, sidewinders come
out from the side windows, and pythons snap at running Moo-Moo customers. The mothers and the snakes
face each other, hissing, dancing, writhing, and
staring.... The mothers taste the sky with their
tongues and sashay slowly, doing a snaky line dance
at the Moo-Moo Derby.

The women of Allegheny hide in the bushes and behind
stacks of candy and antifreeze inside and outside
the Moo-Moo. They rubberneck over each other, video-
ing and peering out at the 2021 Mother's Day Moo-Moo
Derby that has never gone this violent and/or dark.
Flashing yellow and red car lights reflect in the
liquid napalm of the glistening gasoline.... Time
stops... time becomes elevated, or it is finally
respected. Then time floats within the gasoline

fumes that I actually enjoy... because it reminds me
of many miracles I've seen in the past.

Suddenly, there is a flash in the sky like light-
ning, and the Moo-Moo Derby becomes a miracle as an
image of the Virgin Mary floats in the pink ether
gasoline atmosphere above the Moo-Moo!

I rub my eyes in disbelief, as the lonely surrealism
of Appalachia is twisting my *Intel*. I'm not sure
if the Virgin Mary is being reincarnated via the
vapors of gasoline or if I am unfortunately getting
a flashback from some rocking acid I dropped at the
Burning Man (BM) festival ten (10) years ago.

The Virgin Mary floats in oily iridescent colors
above the mothers of poverty and luxury. The poor
Pinto and the macho Mercedes start to also aesthetically morph and trail into some psychedelic-trip.
Without warning, the mothers push the gas and ram
each other with the rear of their cars with such
force and such malice that the Virgin Mary has to
step-in and calm this momentary lapse of reason
with a miracle. The Virgin holds time still.

From a Virgin Mother's room, from this gloom, and
from this doom, my half-wit sisters and mothers
wince, nodding at each other, eyes still locked eye
to eye. Their cars' rear wheels are raised up by
their monumental motherly force. But, instead of
smashing, their cars merge in some time-warp miracle. Barb and Maddy have become autoerotic lesbian *lovers* stuck in an entangled metal embrace.
Barb and Maddy are scissor-fucking at the Mother's
Day Moo-Moo Demolition Derby, and the women of
Allegheny scream in horror. This is the *Other*....

Mad, the sagging selfie-slut, blows a kiss to Barb,
the Kodak-whore. Then Maddy, via her Mercedes's
camera screen in her center console, zooms in with
her touchscreen to watch Barbara staring and glaring back at her. They smoke their cigarettes as the

People's Exhibit N – The Mother's
Day Moo-Moo Demolition Derby

fire station bells whine like wartime sirens in the background. The Allegheny firemen, police, and the Empire are coming.

The large floating hologram of the Virgin Mary still floats in the gray Appalachian sky. The women of Allegheny are on their knees, saying their rosary prayers. Protestant ladies run away in existential horror. Catholic women look very scared, are frozen in place, and in unison start repeating a prayer hard and fast that escalates in volume and gravitas. It starts to sound like a Nazi chant, "Hail Mary, full of grace, the Lord is with thee. Hail Mary, full of grace, the Lord is with thee. Hail Mary, full of grace, the Lord is with thee."

And the few Jewish ladies in Allegheny look around for video projection cords in the bushes in order to pull the curtain back on this "Virgin" bullshit.

Barbara and Madeline's cigarette smoke rises from their mouths... the gasoline flows... it continues to spill and slosh around their car tires.... Madeline and Barbara continue to stare at each other, smelling simultaneously the fresh and volatile Empire gas around *Them*. The Virgin Mary floats in and out of focus. She is looking down at the mothers of luxury and poverty and yawns loudly....

The smoking mothers with their vile stares look like the mother lizards Sophia sent. But the Virgin says nothing and quietly and solemnly looks at each mother for a moment. The large, iridescent, floating Virgin Mary looks like an intense cat as she slowly closes her eyes for a moment, thus communicating that she, the Virgin Mary, trusts and blesses the Appalachian mothers of poverty and luxury and that they can carry on with their motherly business.

The mothers of Allegheny's stares turn into *Mother's Day Madness* grimaces. They both lightly pull on

their cigarettes... each exhaling, playing with
their smoke playfully as they each ash out their
windows.... Here is a miracle, here is *Nothing*...
here, Family Court and Good Reader: here is Mother's
Day in Appalachia 2021.

The Allegheny fire department and police start to
arrive, so I pull out of the 2021 Mother's Day Moo-
Moo Demolition Derby. The target mothers do the
same. I head towards target #21-4532's house.

Chapter 18

6:23 P.M. - MOTHER AND DAUGHTER ARE STRIPPED OF THEIR GARMENTS AND NAILED TO A CROSS, OR, COMPLAINT #21-4532

I'm parked on Dam Road and see and hear on my laptops Barbara, her husband, and her two (2) grandchildren finishing up Mother's Day dinner. The Daltons wonder aloud where Susan has gone, since she ran off blind as a bat, bouncing off cars and trees down Dam Road. Diana, the youngest daughter, sniffles and cries with her head down. She weeps because no one is paying attention to her, and asks, "Where's Mother on Mother's Day?"

The whole neighborhood saw the tragic last dance of Susan Dalton. Where can she be? She wouldn't stand out in Allegheny. Blind, enraged, and drunk is a good citizen in Appalachia. Susan has stayed out for days before. But this is Mother's Day, and Barbara's son is in Attica with all those other incarcerated inmates, wishing they had been better sons and daughters to their mothers. But none of *Them* will call to repent and/or show their motherly *love*. The Empire's inmates stagnate in their retarded license-plate-making Empire State. All of the mothers of Attica, all the sad mothers of

prisoners turn over another year of pain with no
compromise. Revenge rules *Motherhood*; retaliation
governs *Mother's Day Madness.*

As Barbara slowly clears the table, she tears up
before the unused plate and silverware that she had
set for her daughter. Barbara suddenly picks up the
pace in order to shake her sentimental feelings,
but the cleaning of her house is fruitless, and the
tearing turns to sobbing. Something bad is hap-
pening, and the two-hundred-and-sixty-nine (269)
year-old women seems to feel it in her old bones.

Barbara, like *Us* all when we have our radar up for
Intel, has felt this way before. When we close our
eyes, we know the truth. What does our gut say?
What is the right thing to do? What is happiness?
No answer flows from our tongue. We hide, and the
porcupine hugs our hearts; we run, and the wolves
nip at our ankles. Looking for comfort, Barbara
Dalton and some of *Us* look to the Bible. But no holy
book will help Barbara with the knock on the door
that is coming on this Mother's Day evening.

Barbara goes downstairs in her dark earthen crawl
space to snivel and smoke alone. She slowly smokes
a spliff to ease her pain and discontent. About
three quarters (3/4) of the way through, and feeling a little less pain, there is a hard knock on
her front door.

Barbara yells for her husband, "Bill! Bill! Answer
the damned door." The knocks at the front door continue louder and more frequently. Barbara walks up
the broken-down stairs that are more a ladder with
missing rungs than a staircase. The small house
is very dark, as usual, and she peeks out of the
drawn, dirty curtains to see who's knocking so
aggressively... it is the Allegheny Police!

"Fuck," Barbara spits out as she extinguishes her
spliff on the kitchen linoleum floor. She thinks

out loud and says, "What the hell do they want?" Barbara physically spins around in utter confusion... she doesn't know where her husband is or where the grandchildren are. But she hopes someone will help her. Barbara circles back and walks towards the basement — then she walks to the back door and spaces-out for way too long. Then, again, Barb starts walking towards the basement; then she starts to walk upstairs; then, defeated and out of options, Barbara walks to the front door.

Again, the hard, fast *"Knock, knock, knock, knock, knock"* booms through the front door, followed by, "Allegheny Police, please open up, Ms. Dalton; we know you're in there," spoken by a strong female voice from outside the door.

"Shit," Barbara whispers under her breath.

Barbara sprays what she thinks is air freshener, but instead it is the Raid bug spray her daughter blinded herself with earlier. Likewise, Barbara starts coughing and tearing up. Barbara is still looking for an escape from her toxic house, but at the same time, she realizes she is the head of the household legally because her husband has a criminal record.

"Knock, knock, knock" rattles the front door and house again, followed by, "Allegheny Police, please open up," from an intense female voice.

Barbara has to answer the knock on the door, but all she seems to think about is the illegal marijuana garden in the basement. Is she getting raided? She isn't even thinking about her daughter, Susan. Barbara musters up her courage and opens the front door, not so much because she rose to the emergency occasion but because the bug spray is causing her to feel lightheaded.

A female police officer stands awkwardly on Barbara Dalton's "Raft of Poverty." The police officer tries

to find a safe space on the raft, but there is no
safe place in poverty. Realizing this, the female
officer, with a bothered and ignoble contriteness,
asks Barbara, "Are you Barbara Dalton?"

"Yyyesss?" Barbara answers hesitatingly.

The female officer says somewhat joyfully and with
a gleam in her eye, "I've got some bad news for you,
Mrs. Dalton. I'm Officer Swetnam; can I come in?"

Barbara thinks her house smells like marijuana,
so Barbara mumbles something abouts "Cleaning the
house" and does not open the screen door but steps
outside right through the ripped screen within the
screen door.

It is twilight, a crepuscular blue and purple time,
a haunting plum time, with just a smidge of indigo
light and/or hope surrounding the pink and yellow horizon. The positive sun setting... red and
hot, is now somewhere off in western America. Back
here on the scorched-earth threshold of America,
on the Great Hill in Allegheny, overlooking the
western door, where twenty (20) feet of snow falls
every winter and all the smart children leave. Here
in this Appalachian twilight on Barbara's outside
deck, there is only one exposed, garish, fluorescent, outside light that flickers slowly. Its shade
and cover lie in shattered pieces on the ground
below the light. Barbara walks across her "Raft of
Poverty," kicking away beer can empties from her
husband and daughter. Barbara is trying to make
space so they have some room to stand in between
all the trash of cheesy puffs and ant-covered globs
of hamburgers, hotdogs, and macaroni salad.

Barbara says to the female police officer, "Sorry
about the mess."

Officer Swetnam quickly catches Barbara's eye,
interrupting and stopping her silently, as Barbara

is avoiding eye contact. The female police officer makes the universal female questioning noise.
And Family Court and Good Reader, we've all heard
this female alarm throughout time. Officer Swetnam
taunts, sings, and questions at the same time on a
sliding scale ending on a down note, "Mmmmmmmmmmmm
- Hmmmmmmmmmmmm?" The officer of the Empire realizes Barbara isn't sorry about her porch mess. The
officer of the law shuffles her feet and obviously
wants to get this motherly meeting over with as
soon as possible (ASAP). Barbara looks ashamed now,
and she gently bows to the female officer's power
and dominance. Officer Swetnam sighs and shakes
her head, disgusted that she has to deal with the
likes of an arrogant and degenerate mother. Then
the officer says, as if she has said this statement
a thousand times, with a sick smirk, "I'm sorry to
inform you, but I've got some bad news for you.
We've found your daughter, Susan."

Barbara suddenly stands up straight, comes alive,
and says, "You Empire cunt, what did you do with
her?" This is not a strange question, as Susan
being arrested was a quarterly or seasonal event
in Allegheny. Driving while impaired (DWI), drug
possessions (DP), breaking and entering (BE), and
domestic disputes (DD) were the seasons of Susan's
life in Appalachia.

Officer Swetnam says incredulously, "We did nothing. We found her in the abandoned 'USA Made' furniture factory down near the river, not breathing,
after we received an anonymous call. As you know,
the old furniture factory is a known shooting gallery / a drug-use spot, and drug paraphernalia was
found next to Susan's body."

Barbara screams, "You're a liar! What do you mean
she's not breathing? I gave her-her-her life; I
gave her my br-br-br-"

I know she wants to say, "My breath," but she can't.

All that comes out of her mouth is her own breath that reflects against the misty light bulb glare on Barb's "*Raft of Poverty*." Barbara Dalton's breath in the cold night becomes white ghosts like an evaporating electrical force. Barb is an Appalachian mother trying to explain giving birth to her child, but she cannot.

Officer Swetnam says, "We took her to the hospital, but she was pronounced dead on arrival (DOA). We're not sure about the exact cause of death, but I wanted to inform you immediately of her passing. I think the hospital said Susan died of a black heart... we're very sorry for your loss, but we need someone to identify the body as soon as possible (ASAP)."

Barbara Dalton just got her soul caught in a bear-trap... and she starts to unravel. At this moment, in her mind, she begins to run towards death; she is moving beyond the death-drive. Barbara and mother are slipping away from empirical civilization. There is no more positive light for her.... Barbara and her *Motherhood* are a callous centrifugal force going with the buffalo and societal herd, just going along for the ride for the last sixty-two (62) years / for the last two hundred and sixty-nine years (269) years. Barbara screams at the police officer, "A black heart? A black heart, you're a murderer, Swetnam – you and your Empire are murderers!"

Barbara Dalton's life is exposed for the fraud it is. Her motherly life has been an existential joy-ride, a merry-go-round of child abuse. She seems to finally think poignantly to herself: *I'll do anything to end this bullshit mother game... I've had enough. I'll do anything to get off this female ride... anything!*

When Barbara silently realizes there is no easy way out of her situation – her daughter (with two

(2) orphaned children) dying in an abandoned factory on Mother's Day – Barbara starts to heave the
Mother's Day dinner she just prepared for her family. It rises in her larynx, her pores open up, her
stomach rolls, beads of perspiration develop on her
forehead. Barbara writhes like a feral cat about
to give it a good yack. Officer Swetnam is not on
guard; she does not see this coming as Barbara
pukes her Mother's Day meal on Officer Swetnam's
shiny patent-leather shoes and neatly pressed poly-
ester pants and blouse. The chunks of red pimento
from Barbara's macaroni salad contrast nicely with
Officer Swetnam's jet-black, well-polished shoes.
Barbara's four (4) Silver Bullet beers come up also
and splash merrily down the officer's khaki pants,
making the policewoman look like she has peed in
her pants. This at first annoys Officer Swetnam,
an officer of the Empire law, but she regains her
composure, realizing she is a cop on the clock,
there to protect and serve... and periodically to
be puked on.

Barbara is weakened, lost, and poisoned as she
imagines Susan, the mother of her two (2) grandchildren, convulsing and twitching into a coma in
the USA Made factory where she and her husband
worked for twenty-five (25) years. The closing of
the furniture factory killed Allegheny and all its
employees' futures... and now it has killed her
child.... Barbara seems to imagine her daughter all
alone with the opossums, raccoons, and rats that
live in that old, polluted factory. That factory
is home to the homeless and the dead now. The factory employed both Barbara and her husband as young
adults and also their grandparents before that.
That was before the North Atlantic Free-Trade Act
(NAFTA) wiped out Middle America in the Rust Belt
and on all Appalachian Main Streets.

Barbara again imagines her daughter's disjointed
body, with trickles of blood coming out of her
ears, nose, and mouth, at the same factory where

she once made a livable wage twenty (20) years ago.
She thought... *what the hell is the "Allegheny
Gazette" going to write?* But Honorable Family Court
and Good Reader, as I've said before, when you have
the Empire politicians, the press, and the police
all on the same page, all on the same side, all
on the same take, the cold-cash *Intel* take – any
opposition to the Empire / to *Intel,* to the local
furniture company reducing your pay and health benefits is no more – it is hearsay and blasphemy. And
then, because you don't want to be a slave at the
local furniture company, you get fired first.

Barbara declares to Officer Swetnam, "You Empire
cunts aren't just killing me, but now you're killing my children in the same building my future
was killed and replaced in! Is my uselessness not
enough for you? My grandfathers and fathers fighting in your World Wars is not enough? My outsourced
death and angry life is now also criminal because
I rightfully hate and despise you cops for the
Empire? My white civil-less life, my whitey-cracker
non-citizen life? Below and underneath that of an
illegal immigrant — my Appalachian life is too much
that now you have to kill my child also?"

Officer Swetnam answers, "Well, Mrs. Dalton, your
drug-addicted daughter was a slut – she was lewd
and idle – so maybe it's best where she is now.
Sorry, just telling you the truth."

"The truth...?" Barbara questions. "You were friends
in high school; you helped her get addicted to those
drugs and groomed her into a shallow female whore!"

Office Swetnam retorts, "Or perhaps... Barb...
you're just a shitty mother?"

Barbara is paralyzed, frozen, and unable to speak....
She answers that child-abuse accusation without
words, but by retching out her spirit and spitting her soul out of her mouth again. Barbara drops

to her knees on her sinking "*Raft of Poverty*."
Barbara is sweating, heaving, and gasping, trying
to throw-up something / anything, but there is no
more positivity in her body. Barb is slowly being
consumed by an unforeseen blob - the negative space
has tipped the scales, and pessimism is Barb's only
spatial plane.

Barbara and Officer Swetnam float together on this
"Raft of Poverty" and cannibalism in the open ocean.
It is a funeral ship for *Motherhood*, a fall of wom-
anhood! These cannibalistic Appalachian women eye-
ball each other up, imagining one another a plump
pork-chop or an all-you-can-eat buffet at Cracker
Barrel ($4.99 Single Pass Only, While Supplies
Last, and No Doggy Bags). These women on "The Raft
of Poverty" are floating on the luck of nature and
are not looking to be rescued.

Barbara is on her knees with snakes in her hair as
Officer Swetnam starts to rub her back, trying to
keep Barbara's greasy hair from the pool of puke on
the back porch. Barbara looks up, white as a dead
ghost with bloodshot eyes, and begs / pleads with
Officer Swetnam, "Are you sure it's Susan? Have I
lost my daughter; have I lost myself?"

Officer Swetnam is getting bored and not paying
attention as she holds her dead sister, as she
holds her *Sister X*. She says, "The body had no ID
on it, but I knew who it was. Susan and I were in
elementary school together. We played hopscotch
together."

Switching gears quickly, Officer Swetnam asks, "Is
your husband home?"

Barbara doesn't answer the question and quietly, as
if she were talking to her dead daughter far off,
quietly whispers, "Hopscotch...."

At this moment, Craig and Diana, the son and

daughter of the dead mother, Susan, come to the door, looking out of the ripped screen door. They sing in unison in an Appalachian drawl, "Wuus a matta Graaannnmma?"

Barbara spins around on the ground like an automobile-hit marsupial: Barb is mangled, twitching, possessed, and screeching, "Get in the damned house, and go find your damned grandfather! Go! Get, get, get. Go, go, go!!!"

Barbara seems to feel the weight of the many lives she has lived.... The many lives of never getting ahead and always dying worse off from where she started. Barbara struggles to get to her feet and wobbles when the officer of the Empire helps Barbara Dalton stand. And then Swetnam throws Barbara to the ground again mercilessly with another motherly question the officer already knows the answer to.

"Are those Susan's children?" Officer Swetnam asks.

Barbara screeches and growls like a mountain cat caught in a bear-trap. She makes a screeching noise that sounds like chattering or gurgling. Barb collapses again, or should I say, she implodes like a demolished building dynamited at her structural weakest points. Barbara's *Motherhood* collapses upon its own weight. She is blubbering, drooling, and crying... as mucus runs from her nose down into her mouth. Barb is hiccupping, breathing in gulps and spurts as if she is being strangled invisibly and dragged down into the ground... and, in fact, she is.

"Where are the fathers of Susan's children?" Officer Swetnam asks petulantly with an air of smugness.

Barbara looks up with a terrorized rage in her eyes and claws back at the female officer of the Empire law, "Where else, you Empire pig? Fucking Attica!"

And Barbara is absolutely right. Officer Swetnam did know that the multiple fathers of Barbara's grand-children were all in Attica. Policewoman Swetnam, a true guard or officer of patriarchy, is a proud slave within the master-slave dialect. She is an officer of the law, a woman double-agent (like me) representing the law. Officer Swetnam is just ask-ing rhetorical questions of its slaves, just to inflict cruel and unusual punishment. Those of *Us* in the Empire and/or Intel can easily turn our pain into pleasure and live in the wild blue yonder – somewhere between diplomacy, wit, and war.

Officer Swetnam was born a woman but went into the "Law" and became the *Law*. She is on the wrong side of *En-Soi* / *Pour-Soi*; Swetnam is a woman in the law / constructed by the law, and not a woman for the law – or a woman changing the law. Because the law changes with the miniskirt length – the law changes with the wind and whims of man-made "Fashion."

Chapter 19

7:30 P.M. - MOTHER IS LAID IN A TOMB, OR, COMPLAINT #21-6154

I'm back on Highland Avenue for the final stake-out of Complaint #21-6154. My cameras and mics just started fuzzing out on laptop one (1), but my backup Sting-Ray laptop fills in like a champ. I see Hoi-Noi the housekeeper clearing Mother's Day dinner from Madeline's dining-room table. Madeline's husband and two (2) daughters are now being served dessert. Madeline sits at the head of the table, reveling in the faux adoration and sentimental attention. Madeline sits upright in a perky manner as her husband and two (2) daughters play with their phones, texting others very far away from Mother's Day dinner in Allegheny.

Honorable Family Court and Good Reader, I anxiously eject Shania Twain's "Man, I _Feel_ Like a Woman" because things feel like they're about to go sideways here with Complaint #21-6154. I need to stop Shania's musical brainwashing - I think Steve Earle called her "The highest paid lap-dancer in Nashville," which I always thought was funny and accurate, but I still like her.

When I'm in doubt on which way the wind is blowing with life, I return to classical music. Music for the right side of the brain without silly words, like these silly words – all around here.... So, I slide in my impeccably-cared-for CD called "*Appalachian Spring*," 1955, by Aaron Copeland.

This classical musical composition starts so slowly... it's as if we are musically still in the throes of a March winter. The flute and violas drip and drop beautiful green notes and blue tones. The music is icy-blue glaciers melting into a very large, quiet, white underground lake. Here is where I imagine this "*Appalachian Spring*" starts – it is somewhere deep in Antarctica or the North Pole. Curious oboes peek out from their earthen burrows, harps and cellos wiggle out of tree-nests, bassoons remove the rock from their cave, and life exhales a beautiful sigh of spring relief. Then the *allegro* tempo picks up with brisk and lively violins and violas coming to the forefront of this Appalachian spring. The many stringed instruments sing inces-santly and happily like an Appalachian spring or growing green grass at dawn, "Good morning! Good morning! Good morning!"

Aaron Copland's "Appalachian Spring" is a ballet about going West in America; it's about pioneering in America. And in 1955, Martha Graham, the cho-reographer and dancer, not only commissioned this symphony from Copland, but she also danced that American Shaker dance in Washington, D.C. and on television for all the world to see.

The "*Appalachian Spring*" *moderato* playfully picks up speed on my car's sound system as the forlorn Madeline says sheepishly, "Can we have a normal family conversation here?"

No one looks up from their phones. "I'm... hello? Can we be a family here and have a nice Mother's Day dinner conversation?"

Her husband looks up and says, "What, dear? It's just the wind, just the wind."

Madeline tilts her head, opens her mouth, and stares in disgust at her husband's wasteland blow-off response as he continues to text on his phone under the table. Maddy brings her voice down numerous octaves to clue in her husband she isn't fucking around. "Be polite ,for God's sake, it's my goddamned day!" she demands.

"Oh, right, hey kids, put away your phones - your mother's right," her husband responds. The two (2) daughters continue to be engrossed with their phones, a million (1,000,000) miles away from any family member sitting at this Mother's Day dinner. Christa and Michelle look up from their phones, feigning dismay and bewilderment, which pleases Madeline for a moment. Then they both return to their social lives on their phones the very second Madeline turns away.

Hoi-Noi enters the yellow, creamy dining room with a silver tray stacked with luxurious desserts. Madeline acts as if the silver plate of desserts is a birthday cake and she is the birthday girl! Madeline's husband gives Hoi-Noi one of his famous McHugh winks that causes Hoi-Noi to recoil in disgust. Mr. McHugh has had twelve (12) extramarital affairs, including two (2) with Hoi-Noi over the last nine (9) years.

Hoi-Noi, Madeline's most faithful family member, walks over to Madeline, offering a choice of either a piece of lemon meringue pie, key lime pie, or pecan pie. Madeline picks the pecan pie, and a Mother's Day halo appears around her head. Madeline glows and sinks at the same time. Hoi-Noi goes around to the other family members, offering delicate pie slices. Everyone shoos Hoi-Noi away with a disgruntled wave of the hand or a head nod.

Mr. McHugh says, "I'm way over my calories today; I can't." Madeline starts shaking with rage that her husband is not taking part in the Mother's Day party. Yet, no one sees that the birthday girl is about to throw a tantrum: *Mother's Day Madness* is about to blow a gasket.

Madeline starts wolfing / eating / shoveling in her pecan pie as tears stream down her cheeks, forming little puddles on her clean, crisp, folded, undisturbed napkin. Salty tears slide off her fancy silver teaspoon and hit her pie plate. The red carnation Madeline pinned to her breast is littered with pecan pie crumbs. The carnation, like a Venus flytrap, seems to grab the brown crumbs. The red carnation suddenly curls-up, curling inwards, ingesting the pecan invaders. No one at the table notices, as they are all back to texting / playing games with imaginary friends on the matrix of the faux *Real*. Instead of rescuing their Me-Generation mother from the torture of *Mother's Day Madness*, Maddy's family members are obsessed with themselves. Mad's children were left behind with no discipline, responsibility, and/or respect for life or other humans. These discontented deadbeat children of luxury respect only money.

Madeline reaches over and grabs three (3) or four (4) of the remaining chocolate candies her husband lovingly gave her. These candies are the last of three (3) large boxes of candies because her daughters and husband ate the other eighty (80) or so Mother's Day candies. Nonetheless, Madeline shoves these chocolates in her mouth haphazardly, some with the light red and silver foil still on the candy. Madeline also shovels another pile of pecan pie and whipped cream in her mouth in order to temporarily dull the sharp, metallic, emotional pain.

Madeline sits there, finally relaxed and at peace.... Madeline is out of her body; Madeline is out of her mind and deep into *Mother's Day*

Madness. Maddy starts to choke lightly. Maddy confidently swigs her champagne from a crystal flute.
Mad rolls her neck, loosens up, and seems psyched
about her descent. Mad looks stoked as she embraces
her madness. Mad's Little Object A, Object B, and
her Little Deaths are exploding like psychological
fireworks in her dark soul. Maddy, forgetting about
her pleasure drive, now way beyond the death drive,
squeals, "Wwweeeeeee!!" with abandoned, child-like
glee.

To receive a gift on Mother's Day that you don't
deserve and have it served up on a silver plat-
ter doesn't sit well with all women. There is no
honesty, no sentiment in Mother's Day 2021 – only
profit.

The champagne and bonbons and pie start to come
back up Madeline's esophagus as fast as they went
down. Madeline looks like she starts to taste and
smell her own bile of her stomach acid in her
mouth. Maddy's upper respiratory system, chest, and
shoulders undulate, heave, and roll in rhythm with
a gack, a skip, and a glitch. Maddy regurgitates
again... Maddy retches again... Maddy's heart seems
to be slowing, a slowing heartbeat, and then dead
air... no rhythm.

No one at Madeline's dinner table notices their
mother dying, except Hoi-Noi, who is frozen and
awestruck by the coming tsunami. Unable to speak,
Hoi-Noi just stares at Madeline gasping for air.
Madeline is very much with her family and very much
completely alone, as no one pays any attention to
Madeline today, or any other day. Hoi-Noi, frozen, is also pouring coffee into Madeline's husband's coffee cup, which now is overflowing onto
the table, unbeknownst to anyone.

Madeline looks around her dining room tomb, sur-
rounded by her passive-aggressive family and wonders

aloud," Will anyone identify (ID) my body at the Empire State Mother's Day morgue?" No one answers....

The hot coffee Hoi-Noi pours is ripping hot, and it pools into a large puddle directly in front of Madeline's husband. Hoi-Noi, frozen out of her wits, fuels the coffee waterfall that now is falling onto Mr. McHugh's lap. Hoi-Noi is still pouring coffee into his overflowing coffee cup. Mr. McHugh's fine woolen tweed pants are not going to stop second (2nd) degree burns about two (2) seconds away over his thigh and groin area.

The wet / electric shock of the steaming-hot coffee in her husband's pants, who still is texting up until this very moment, makes him instantly jump up / fall backwards off his chair and yell, "My Giovanni pants. What the hell?" as he falls to the floor. He rolls around, gets back up, and stumbles away, holding his dear crotch while running out of the Mother's Day mausoleum, still yelling, "My good tweed pants? My beautiful Giovannis! What the hell? What the fuck? I'll never get this stain out."

Hoi-Noi remains frozen even after scorching her master's penis. She continues to pour the remaining coffee on the mahogany dining room table ($11,499) and the fine Italian rug ($8,500). Hoi-Noi stares, transfixed in disbelief, at Madeline, who is turning blue and falling deeper into cardiac arrest as Maddy's coffee pot drips its last drop.

Michelle, Madeline's middle daughter, takes off her headphones and looks up from her phone. Her father has run away from the dinner table like a waddling duck holding his crotch area, screaming something she can't understand.

Michelle looks at Hoi-Noi, the spilled coffee, and Hoi-Noi's frozen pose as if she is pouring coffee for someone. Michelle then looks at her mother, who is trying to stand up for the last time. Maddy

wobbles with whipped cream and bloody vomit drib-
bling down from her face as she grabs tightly to
the dining-room tablecloth.

Madeline clutches and curls the dining-room tablecloth with both hands, bringing the tablecloth to
her chest / to her heart. The silverware and silver dishes start to fall away from the table, as
Madeline wants to take a mortal nap and needs an
existential snuggy blanket. Madeline seems to think
her dining-room tablecloth will do fine for her
next ride, and as usual, Mother Nature is right.
Madeline reaches deep into her small thirteen (13)
year-old soul and gives it all she has for this
final sister-ass rinse, cycle, spin, and spit.

Madeline, standing now, choking and spitting,
finally has got Christa's full attention. Only
because Christa's face is sprayed with bits of her
mother's vomit on the side of her face. Christa,
with her headphones still on, wipes off the orange
chunks and stomach acid mist from her mother's rot-
ted gut and hysterical life.

Christa slowly looks at her mother for the last time
and shrieks, "Eeeeuuuuuwwwwww, Madeline, you're
gross!" Then Christa runs out of the dining-room
tomb.

Hoi-Noi, standing still with an empty silver coffee pot in her hand, is now awake from Christa
running away. Hoi-Noi looks over to Michelle, not
saying a word, and slowly backs up till she is out
of the room. Then she turns and runs. Michelle,
after watching Hoi-Noi, mimics her and also gets up
and slowly backs up because Michelle realizes her
mother is dying in front of her.

Madeline, the statue of *Mother's Day Madness*, is
all alone now in her mausoleum. I see the 911 call
go through on my scanner. The tower of *Motherhood*
in Allegheny is a "9-1-1 call on Mother's Day!" The

envy of young women who played with Barbie dolls, the antithesis of lonely spinsters, the denouncer of the women's Equal Rights Amendment (ERA) in 1979, the condemner of spells and infertility, the crusader against witches, slowly starts to tilt and lean. Madeline, like Barbara, also drifts helplessly on "The Raft of Medusa." But here in luxury, the cannibals will also eat you alive on "The Raft of Luxury."

Maddy's blue skin turns blackish, like her swollen tongue flailing about. Mad's Palm-Beach-blond hair turns into yellow Mamba snakes that writhe upon her head as she transcends into the next dimension.

Madeline Medusa the Empress wobbles like a leaning tower, and she then collapses, taking the entire Mother's Day dining-room table, silverware, glassware, and centerpiece flower display with her. Maddy has gone off the deep end, but she clings to her dear yet fleeting life. This beautiful Dutch Queen from the Netherlands, this good-old hag, here in America over one hundred and twenty-six (126) years before our Revolution, is still looking to get some "Action," like all good Dutchies from New York. Madeline's DNA isn't that of a daughter of the American Revolution (DAR); no, Maddy is a great-grandmother of the American Revolution. But that was then, and now in 2021, Mad has lost it all. She is incarcerated in a *Real* McDonald's (MCD) life for women who chew imported gum sold exclusively on Quality Value Convenience (QVC) television. Madeline's motherly McMansion home has aged her. Then her McHome transformed into a McNursing Home, which quickly is descending down into her McCoffin.

As the first dessert plates and glassware shatter on the hard oak floor, Madeline floats in a free fall.

Within the free fall of *Mother's Day Madness* is the madness of heredity, the madness of family life,

the madness of family tradition. The madness of
family dinners, the madness of family trust, the
madness of it all: family presents, family tribes,
family governments. The madness of "Family *love*,"
ghosting for "Empire *Love*." Madeline hits the floor
with a sickening thud.

Here the square-head *Red-Queen* makes her last move
with her Dutch hardwood clog made more to destroy
than to be worn. Madeline, the noble savage, throws
her wooden clog into the *Motherhood* water mill, and
it crushes the wheel and cog gears in an instant.
The water mill's gears explode in wooden shards and
splinters. The mill stops abruptly with the catastrophic sound of the three hundred (300) trees
needed to build the mill – exploding and hitting
the ground. Maddy gloats as if destruction is
good. The civilized sound of the water mill gears
has been replaced by the meditative sound of the
river water flowing... Mad, the motherly anarchist,
sighs, "Finally, some peace...."

Silver plates, fine China, crystal glassware, and
antique silverware rain down upon Maddy's head like
a much-needed rain.

Italian glasses, English silverware, Irish cream-
ers, and fine linen napkins float around Madeline
as she bounces, shakes, and convulses into cardiac arrest on her dining-room floor. Madeline is
still all alone in slow-motion. Maddy then, like
her red carnation, closes in on herself. Mad in a
fetal position covers herself with her existential
tablecloth.

Madeline snuggles for survival. She brings the
tablecloth blanket around her body and curls it in,
close to her heart. Blood starts to trickle from
her nose and mouth. Maddy stares ahead with the
eyes of a dead dog. The blue / gray fog of death
has risen to her eyes, and her final resting spot
is going to be underneath her dining-room table.

Madeline is paralyzed, but she blinks furiously and looks around in a spastic and erratic manner on her deathbed. Maddy is still conscious within the Empire State, and she looks around at the uneaten tea cakes that lie scattered all around her on the dining-room floor. Mad seems annoyed... as the rage and revenge of a sixteen (16) year-old brat boils up in her sixty-two (62) year-old eyes. This is *Mother's Day Madness*.

Madeline growls her last words on earth not as a wish, but as a curse, spitting out amongst gurgles and gasps for air, "Ha, Ha, Urrgurl, Happy, Uuggh, Happy Mother's Day to U, to U... Happy Mother's Day to *Us*!"

I can hear the sirens off in the distance; the Empire is coming. Madeline is dead in her twelve-thousand (12,000) square foot McMansion, which now has instantaneously become her twelve-thousand (12,000) square-foot McCoffin. I slowly drive past the ambulances and police cars rushing past me... hoping to revive a cold, dead Mommy Dearest.

All I can hear are Madeline's last words: "Happy Mother's Day to *Us*!" As I drive away, all I can think is: "Who is *Us*? Is *Us* mothers? Is *Us* motherhood? Or is *Us* all of the lonely, abused wives with mean and misogynist husbands? Is *Us* all the moms who walk and/or endure with constant perseverance?"

Chapter 20

<u>Chapter 20</u>

9:58 P.M. - <u>A REVELATION? A MIRACLE? OR MAYBE, JUST A COMPLAINT?</u>

Honorable Family Court and Dear Reader, I'm on the
highway headed back east to Albany on this Mother's
Day night. I'm poking along at fifty-five (55)
miles per hour (mph) in the slow lane. I'm trying
to catch my breath.... I've watched a LOT of people die in front of me, but watching Madeline pass
tonight has hurt me deeply.

It's almost 10:00 p.m., and the night is my friend
once again. The highway forms an alley away from
the Western door of America, and I'm on the highway feeling good, as the best part of being in
Appalachia - is leaving Appalachia.

The clear night is purple-black, but the spring
stars are out. I roll down my window and smell the
Adirondack pines stretching and growing away from
the cold scorched earth. A warm breeze from the
mid-Atlantic earth pushes the Canadian winds back
for a moment or so. I think again about Madeline's
wish for *Us*, wondering why she didn't say "to me"?
Was Madeline's sixteen (16) year-old soul finally

thinking in a collective, female way on her death-bed? This realization is haunting me.

It's clear within the third-world of Central America and the Middle East, who trade abuse as a currency, exactly who *Us* and *Them* are. And back in the Empire, back in the blue states and capital cities, *Us* and *Them* and the abuse is obvious. But as I drive away from the *Real* America, the Great Hill, the Western Door to America, and from the Lady of the Lake at Chautauqua – I'm troubled about *Us* and *Them.*

Was Madeline speaking to herself as the *Other*? Was *Motherhood* within luxury talking to *Nothing* or the *Real?* Was luxurious mother psychotic or a sociopath? Schizophrenic, bipolar... or both? Had Madeline's guilt become the *signifier* of her *Real*? Was Madeline's lavishness a paranoid and perverse loop? Was she in contact with her unraveled *Sister X*, our female-variable chromosome unchained? Did she have any respect for herself?

Luxurious *Motherhood* ascends into purgatory, which has the same clay-colored sky of Allegheny.... Maddy, the limping camel, is going to try to slip through the eye of heaven's needle... thinking she's entering the kingdom of God. Sorry to say, I don't think luxurious *Motherhood* and all her children will ever enter the kingdom of God.

Honorable Family Court and Dear Reader, I want to thank you for your time in reading this deposition. As I conclude this novel deposition, please mark my words. My fifteen (15) People's Exhibits here in these Complaints are certain and mathematical about the Appalachian child abuse I have witnessed. If you Good Readers are also Good Lookers, you will see how my illustrations and paintings draw-out the unspeakable, the unsaid. I telepathically communicate what is n o t said in this text. I communicate to you, Good Looker, through your third (3ʳᵈ) eye and gut. I communicate what is in the space in between these written lines of silly letters, words, and spaces of black-and-white blobs to the right side of your brain.

My ink, charcoal, and watercolors will have a long, interesting drink with you, or perhaps... a psyche-delic smoke? Or maybe we will share a curious and enlightening afternoon tea? Perhaps we will get a runner's high during an exhausting run at dusk? Or perchance at dawn? And maybe my drawings fall into a sweaty shag after a long night partying, or per-haps a warm candlelit bath after a long day? And in this sixth (6th) dimension dream state... is where I sometimes live.

I live here because it's quiet, it's where we are all going, and it gives me answers in a free-grace manner. But I must confess that I'm still a muddled woman puzzled about *Us* and *Them*. Am I in Markazi, Managua, or Allegheny? It doesn't matter – I'm still baffled about the *Real,* and who *Us* and *Them* are. As women in the *Real,* we overestimate our internal factors and underestimate the external factors. Our *Sister X* delusion becomes reality, and we believe a man's bullshit (BS) about *Us.* But in the sixth (6th) dimension, misogyny, *bravado*, and *machismo* do not exist.

With unfriendly and lifeless men on my mind on this Mother's Day night, I remember the last letter I carry and hold closest to me in my M-8888 satchel. It is from November 1948, Philadelphia – three (3) months before my grandmother died. It is from a young fan of my mother's good work after she was institutionalized for speaking out against raising children into soldiers to die for needless wars. The letter is from a little orphan girl who sewed a nickel ($0.05) onto a pulpy piece of paper and sent in the nickel ($0.05) as a donation to help get my grandmother out of the sanitarium. The found-ling girl didn't have a name and went by "Girl X" because that's what she signed as her name. *Girl*

X appreciated the Mother's Day clubs my mother ran. These clubs would tour the local Philadelphia orphanages every week. My grandmother Anna Jarvis would tell the foundlings, orphans, and misfits – "You are not forgotten, but do not be sentimental. Your mothers who abandoned you were BAD mothers, and they should ALL BE FORGOTTEN! We only have one mother here on earth – and that mother is Sophia, and/or Mother Nature."

Girl X would jump up and roar, "Three (3) cheers for Mother Nature!" And she would have the entire orphanage behind her singing, "Hip-hip hooray, hip-hip hooray, hip-hip hooray."

Girl X was a precocious little orphan "Annie" or "Oliver," always wanting "More" of my grandmother's stew. Girl X reminds me of Nathaniel Hawthorne's "Pearl" in "*A Scarlett Letter*," who Nathaniel Hawthorne described as, "The child, a mischievous airy sprite, an outlaw – whose very existence is the breaking of our law."

When Girl X heard my grandmother was thrown into the psychiatric State Hospital (next to the Foundling Hospital), she and many other fans of the origi-nal Mother's Day mission (Mothers Ending War) sent money to help my mother get out of the looney-bin. Philadelphia, the supposed city of brotherly and sisterly *love*, had taken my grandmother away in a paddy-wagon, away to solitary confinement, because she believed in mothers standing up against the abusers of their children.

Girl X wrote a letter around her crudely sewn nickel ($0.05) donation:

> **Dear Ms. Jarvis,**
>
> **I really like you. I really miss you. I want more! You always seem like one of us at the**

dinners... we're all alone now — where did
you go?

I know I not always good, but I keep you on
your toes. I also like your stories, I like
you serious, I like you smile when I make you
laugh. I like you angry when I'm bad. I like
you mean and crazed when we clean.

You make good gruel! You smell nice! You give
me hope when there is none. Where are you?
Are you one of Us? The forgotten? An orphan?
An outlaw / a misfit now? Living as a nothing? A nobody? It's not bad... if you waste-
not and want-not.

I really like you. I really miss you so much!

I will put the white carnation you gave me on
my orphan prison windowsill. You do the same on
your mother prison window, and our white carnations will talk – our carnations will not blind
men; our carnations will help men see clearly!

I hope your prison better than mine... we can
dream of escaping together! For now... you
are definitely one of us!

I hope my nickel help you get out!

I stole, I... I mean, I borrowed the nickel
from my house mother - no sister to us....

I send you back all the hope and respect you
gave me.

Thank You... Forever!

Your Little,

Sister X

Dear Ms. Jarvis,   November 3rd, 1948

I really like you. I really miss you. I WANT MORE! You alway seem like one of us at the dinners. WE'RE all alone now. Where did you go?

I know I not always good, but I keep you on your toes. I like your stories. I like you serious, I like you SMILE when I make you laugh. I like you angry when I'm bad. I like you mean and crazed when we clean.

You make good gruel! You SMELL NICE! You give me hope when there is none. Where did you go? Are you one of us? The forgotten? An orphen? An outlaw now? A misfit now?

I really like you, so I will put the carnation you gave me on my prison windowsill. Do the same on your prison window and our carnations will talk!

I hope your prison better than mine... we can dream of escaping together. You are one of us!

I hope my nickel ——→

help you get out!

I stole, I... I mean, I borrowed the nickel from my house mother, no SISTER to us!

I send you back all the hope and respect you gave me, THANK YOU FOREVER,
     Your Little,
     SISTER X

People's Exhibit O –
Letter from Little Sister X

I need some good music now for the last leg of my *Mother's Day Madness* mission. This dark drive back east to capital reality and the *Real* is a cooling ointment from the hot, endless fire of Appalachia. All my thinking about the *Us* and *Them* theory on this trip has me suddenly questioning why I am not listening to Pink Floyd's "Dark Side of the Moon." On this 1973 musical *magnum opus* album, there is an incredible song called "Us and Them."

Some of you Good Readers may also be Good Listeners, so you will know what I'm talking about when I skip through Pink's "Dark Side" classics: "Breathe," "Time," and "Money" in order to get to the B-side power ballad of "Us and Them."

"Us and Them" starts off as a single note – it's a lonely out-of-tune organ oscillating in a big stone church. I can control the CD playback speed and cut the song to about half of its original speed. "Us and Them" is now at around sixty-five (65) beats per minute (BPM). This rate of rhythm is slower than our heart rate and perfect for right-brain medi-tation and exploration. The "Us and Them" organ-ist is still lost fiddling with a thought, find-ing the right notes in a sequence while the cold wind blows through the drafty church. The organist plays thoughts and notes not in a sequence, but maybe the notes and thoughts should be in a rhythm. Regardless, it is the sequence the organist con-templates. The tuning organist is now in a sad and salty lighthouse sending out a friendly frequency to all good sailors – the lighthouse, shines gen-tly, softly, and for miles with every turn of the light high on top of the lighthouse. The light emu-lates, "I need a friend, I need a friend, I need a friend."

As the song continues, not just one (1) friend, but two (2) friends pop-up on the horizon. It's Mr. Bass and Mr. Drums in a little rowboat synced to the waves. They come see-sawing into the musical composition with the organist like long-lost ship-mates. Organ, drums, and bass immediately fall into each other's musical arms and embrace in "*Us and Them*." There they roll on the seashore soundscape of frequencies in ethereal bliss when out of the blue, a sexy and sassy sax takes us to another world.

The sax is obviously a frequent-flyer in the mile-high club, most definitely first class. The sexy sax takes *Us* higher, higher, and higher! We then musically hit a cloud, a plateau, leaving that damp and drafty church of "Us and Them" way behind. The cloud is white, airy, and has faint horizon lines as the "Us and Them" lyrics in big, black, block lettering float down from the dark side of the moon. The dark, black letters and words slowly pass me on my little cloud and fall slowly to the earth below. Pink Floyd's words echo for eternity... And Good Listener, you know how this moonglow dirge goes. It starts with echoing words. Does it start with *Us* or *Them*? I think it's: *Us, Us, Us,* and *Them, Them, Them.* And then it asks if we're ordinary men, men, men, men. It asks *Us* what we would choose to do, do, do, do.

I'm passing the town called Friendship and/or Harmony and just realized that this is the *Gas Station Man*'s exit. I bet he will have an interest-ing take on *Us* and *Them....*

I drive past two Empire state troopers side-sad-dled up to each other in the middle median of the highway. These Empire bullies are ready to strike in any direction. This is how police states operate in Markazi, Managua, or Appalachia. The Empire is two bulls watching each other's rear — spinning, protecting each other's flanks. Here on the high-way in America, We, or *Us,* are all travelers, and the Empire troopers are always *Them*. But when you get off the highway, when we slow down, it gets weird. It's the commitment - it's the stand you

must make... and the tax you must pay. It is the
penance and/or a useless Complaint we must file.

I slow down and pull into the *Gas Station Man's*
service station. The falling sugar snow early this
morning made it seem like moths were flying around
the bare station light bulb. Tonight, it's signifi-
cantly warmer, and real moths are drifting around,
looking like downy snowflakes floating in the wind.
These moths tonight search for a truthful light, but
they, too, are deceived. The moths search for the
North Star and are beguiled by the moon, the sun, or
anything bright, warm, and hopeful. The moths are
flittering about... lost in a dark and moist early
spring night. The station's bare light bulb seems
like a lonely twinkling little star in a black-hole
sky. Here I am in nighttime Appalachia at the bottom of the Finger Lakes looking for *Intelligence*
on *Us* and *Them*. And for some reason, I know *Gas
Station Man* will enlighten me.

I pull open the door, and the cowbell and jingle
bells take me back to the merchants and markets
in Afghanistan and Nicaragua. The *Real* cowbell,
taken off a *Real* ox, bull, or cow. The jingle bells
unhooked from a *Real* horse. The bells hang with
fishing wire that has the color of blue mouthwash.
The smell of burned coffee, cigarette smoke, and a
vacant, greasy, auto garage pass over my lips and
up my nose... I am back home again. The TV crack-
les and garbles the calling of an Off-Track Betting
(OTB) horse race as some rodents rustle in the
garbage filled with potato chip bags and Twizzler
wrappers. I walk over towards the coffee pot and
see *Gas Station Man* hunched over his TV, cigarette,
and beer again. I only fill up the cup halfway and
water the coffee down with milk — I am going back
to the Capital; I need to get balanced.

A door to the auto garage opens slightly, and in
comes that majestic Maine Coon cat that hissed at
me earlier. She strolls right past me as if I'm not

here. Her head is almost up to my knee as I don't
move a muscle. The cat stops and starts eyeing me
up and down in a disapproving manner. The cat knows
I am dull and not as perceptive as she. The large,
nimble cat jumps up on a candy shelf, banks off the
empty nacho dispenser, and leaps up to a catwalk
encircling this entire dilapidated retail space.
The retail shop smells like an oil dump-station as
the door to the garage swings and creaks a squeaky
tune because the cold winter drafts are still bat-
tling it out with new warm spring breezes. The
large, powerful cat slithers along above *Us* on the
catwalk towards the *Gas Station Man*. She then tucks
herself in upon herself, slowly and gracefully,
above her master's domain like a noble gargoyle.

I approach the counter, eyeing the cat, and ask,
"Did your mom like your Mother's Day gift?"

Gas Station Man bumbles and tumbles around like a
bear with his paw in the honeypot, saying over and
over, "Oh my God, it's the Empire Lady, oh my God,
it's the Empire Lady, oh my God, it's the Empire
Lady." He straightens up, puts out his cigarette
in his beer again, wipes off his right hand on his
bathrobe, and puts out his hand for a handshake. He
looks me in the eye and says, "You are an angel of
the Lake, you are an angel of Chautauqua."

I shake *Gas Station Man's* hand and say, "I can only
hope."

Gas Station Man exclaims, "You got me off my ass
last night! And my mother will die thinking I *love*
her because of you!"

Gas Station Man laughs deeply and speaks the truth
unknowingly, "Ha, ha, ha, Mother's Day... give me a
break. Ha, ha, ha, whadda load of crap."

I think to maybe agree with *Gas Station Man* and
say, "We moms have to protect *Us*," but I am stopped

out by my truthful mind, by my Intel mind. Instead, I double-dripped out a void of dead air in a void and/or dead-air in a descending tone, "Yeah, total crap, but U-U-U- we moms have to protect U-U-U... sometimes...."

Honorable Family Court and Dear Reader, please use caution when reading my words. Obviously, you just saw in the paragraph above... I cannot say the word "*Us*" in public. I must confess, I cannot say "*Us*" out loud... or in public. This deposition novel may be from an unreliable witness. This deposition novel may be from a hostile witness.

The large cat above *Us* sits up on alert, looking disappointed and disapprovingly down at me like a jealous woman because the *Gas Station Man* is so happy to see me. *Gas Station Man* says, "My mother is always expecting me to miss Mother's Day for the last one hundred and three (103) years, and every Mother's Day, I make it by the skin of my teeth."

Gas Station Man lights a new cigarette and puts out his arms to show me his fine service station. He looks around at his dingy shop and proudly pro-claims: "Where would we be without mothers?" as cigarette smoke puffs out of his mouth with every syllable.

I nod my head, agreeing, "Yeah... absolutely."

I scan the place, looking around at the lotto cards, the trashy gun magazines, the erectile dysfunction (ED) pills, and the marijuana rolling papers. I next look at the cat scowling down at me, a lot of porno magazines, that derelict St. Paddy's cake with fake carnations. I breathe in and, of course, I smell that God-awful Appalachian smell of cat-piss and used oil...

I agree with *Gas Station Man*, exclaiming, "Moms around the world should be proud!"

Gas Station Man puffs up and says with a humble
air, "I try every day." He then quickly turns into
the Appalachian hustler I know he has to be in
order to be running this little Dirty-Gerty gas
station right here in Harmony, America. *Gas Station
Man* leans over the counter and whispers as if we're
being listened to:

"How was the Western Door? Where's the white carnation I gave you showing respect? Did the Seneca
seduce you? Did you pay the toll of white carnations and go through their Western Door to America?
Or did the Seneca try to pluck out your eyes and
steal your soul?"

"Yes," I reply, "the Indians absolutely took my
white carnation as respect, and I saw another white
carnation floating in a parking lot puddle at dawn
- you helped *Us* tremendously."

I continue, "But I have to admit, sir, it was a
hellish time out there. It's still bloody at the
Western Door... I only stood on the threshold of
Allegheny and looked west out at America for eighteen (18) hours or so. I couldn't tell who *Us* was
and who *Them* was out there."

Gas Station Man retorts, "Sounds like you seen
the Seneca wolf-ghost, Empire Lady... I'm just the
Finger Lake ferry man, ma'am, I'm a rock on a spit,
just keeping the light on so sailors can steer their
ships." *Gas Station Man* concludes, "But I will tell
you this: those Seneca are part of the Empire — don't
let them fool you... it certainly is *Us* against
Them."

I say, "*Us* and *Them*?" out loud, but I think to
myself... back on the highway, I know who *Us* and
Them are, and in a strange place with cowbells
and gas stations without gas, I know who *Us* and
Them are. But really... out here in scorched-earth

America and Appalachia, *Us* and *Them* is blurred... *Us* and *Them* is the same.

The silence is kind of awkward but spacious... I look down at my milky coffee on the counter and say, "How much do I owe you, Ferry Man?"

The Finger Lake ferry man replies kindly, "This trip is on me, Empire Lady."

I tease him, "Ah, come on, I'm the *Big Spenda*, I'm the Empire Lady, and I'm going back to the Albany Capital... what can I do for you? Can I give you an Empire revelation? Can I bestow upon you an Empire miracle? Or maybe I can I submit an Empire Complaint that will surely be put on top of the pile."

The ferry man contemplates this Empire offer for a while as he opens a bag of beef jerky and starts chewing on a meat-stick like a bear after hibernating for a winter. Ferry Man offers me a stick, and I decline. He then says in a slow hee-haw Appalachian drawl I *love* to hear, "A revelation, a miracle, or maybe just a Complaint? Hhhhhmmmmmmm... revelations are too subjective, and I ain't one for complaining while I live here in this heaven on earth God has so graciously given *Us*... but an Empire miracle? Can you bring me an Empire miracle?"

I say, "The Empire in the Capital is the miracle-maker."

Gas Station Man leans over the counter, looks at my shoes, smirking like a Cheshire cat. He is shaking his head, looking me up and down, not in a sexual way, but in a psychological / Grandpa / *Intel* way. "Well," he says as if to better understand a new-me by looking at my shoes. "My little Empire Lady, who is doing so well with *Them*, what can *Us* – that being all the lonely people within the Empire – ask for except a date with the royal Empire. That being you, Empire Lady, and/or *Them*."

Gas Station Man continues to lobby for an *Us* and *Them* date. He declares, "We can go to the horse races at Tioga, and we can bet it all on Lady Chautauqua — the horse for *Us*! Appalachia, America, *Upstate* America, and Us will be clearly defined. Our road shall be clear. We will be reborn with your Empress luck - reincarnated by betting it all on *Us* instead of *Them*!"

I chuckle and say, "My luck is *Intelligence.*"

The ferry man holds up his finger as if to quickly caution me about *Intelligence.* He replies, "Beware, strong angel, use caution, double-agent angel, beware, oh mother angel of the lake, where one *loves* it and kills it at the same time. Don't you know the little saying? Why, you must know that little ditty? Why of course... being a mother and part of the Empire, you must know the truth? How does it go? What is it now?"

At that moment, the Maine Coon cat above *Us* stretches her long, cheetah-like haunches and yawns in my face, showing me her wide, pink jaws and vicious teeth. The cat keeps her eyes on me as she licks the side of her paw before she wipes her face up and down numerous times. The cat seems to be grooming and preparing herself for a nighttime mission or hunt. The large, beautiful cat nonchalantly sashays along the high catwalk still looking down at me. The cat slowly growls from its belly and then cries / meows as if threatened and insulted at the same time. The large cat's eyes stay focused on mine as she disappears out the high, broken transom window into the purple, black, and blue Appalachian night. I think to myself - *Constant Perseverance*.

The *Gas Station Man* never acknowledges the large mountain cat walking along the ceiling of his store. Then suddenly, as if emerging from a foggy daydream, *Gas Station Man* blurts out: "Oh, that's right: 'Those that findeth luck, will loseth luck.'"

I say, "Wow... *Intelligence* as luck, or is it luck as *Intelligence*? And tonight, on such a fitting Mother's Day in the Empire State night, why don't you put *Us* and *Them* into the formula, *Sir Gas Station Man?*"

Gas Station Man's hope is born again with his new knighthood and my algebra. He proudly declares, using his nub of beef jerky as a sword of Harmony within the debauchery of the Empire, **"Those that finedeth *Us* will loseth *Us* – and those that findeth *Them* will loseth *Them*."**

We both laugh heartily at our discovered enlightment and/or our *Intel*. I exit his store with my arms extended and my open palms facing the heavens as I exclaim in Appalachian jubilance, "Amen, *Gas Station Man, AAAaaammmen!*"

The hanging silver and gold doorbells jingle and jangle against the glass door as it slams shut, and I, too, go out into the purple, black, and blue Appalachian night. I think to myself – *Constant Perseverance*.

20403734R00154